The Return to Me after **ME**

With fond memories of
my years running and
racing with the Hogweed Trotters.
It was the friendliest
and most welcoming club
I have ever belonged to.

In remembrance of
my dear friend
Bob Bell
xx

Trinity Buckley

The Return to Me after ME

An Athlete's Journey Through Myalgic Encephalomyelitis to Recovery and Beyond

TRINITY BUCKLEY

Matador
Unit E2 Airfield Business Park,
Harrison Road, Market Harborough,
Leicestershire LE16 7UL
Tel: 0116 279 2299
Email: books@troubador.co.uk
Web: www.troubador.co.uk/matador
Twitter: @matadorbooks

ISBN 978-1-80514-044-3

British Library Cataloguing in Publication Data.
A catalogue record for this book is available from the British Library.

Printed and bound in Great Britain by 4edge Limited
Typeset in 12pt Minion Pro by Troubador Publishing Ltd, Leicester, UK

Matador is an imprint of Troubador Publishing Ltd

To my grandchildren
Kyle, Logan and Bella.
Shine bright.

CONTENTS

FOREWORD

I met Trinity when she took part in the Ultra-marathons that my wife Jen and I used to organise back in 2011. At first, she was just another face in the sea of runners but as the year progressed, she seemed to emerge and blossom from the crowd and quickly became one of the people to watch in our nine-race championship. At that time I didn't know her back story, I just saw a person enjoying the many challenges running Ultra-marathon brings and witnessed a champion in the making first hand. A great and worthy champion indeed.

Like Trinity, I was born in the early sixties and my early years were spent in a decade of change in the world. I naively thought that everything would always turn out okay and that the sun would always be shining. Except the world simply isn't like that. Things go wrong. People we love or want to love us, don't. And things didn't turn out the way we planned.

Our lives were mapped out ahead of us in the seventies, or that's how it felt to me anyway. The hurdles of education, employment and relationships were endured, negotiated and explored where again, things didn't go to plan. And when they didn't, it was considered weak to reach out and ask for help or admit defeat and suffer the ridicule of not being a success. It's no wonder people suffered silently with depression and had to find their own solutions to situations that we can now treat effectively with therapy and medication. I know I struggled massively in the late eighties and early nineties and felt lost.

Having reached my own 'Point Zero' as I call it, the lowest point that you can get to in one's mental health, back in 1994, I understand and can sympathise with Trinity about how she felt undertaking her own life journey. I also know what it feels like to know that all you need to do, is to simply 'go for a run' to make things start to feel better – especially when alcohol and self-harming make things worse instead of making them better. Both provide a mere moment's respite in a world of mental and physical pain I found.

Life isn't perfect, far from it. We are programmed from an early age to be the perfect scholar, perfect child, perfect partner and even perfect parent and when we're not, we see ourselves as failures compared to those around us, who we see as being perfect or having the perfect lifestyle.

In 2016, I became very ill with a rare neurological condition called Guillain–Barré Syndrome where I was paralysed from the neck down and had to learn to walk again. I endured a five-month period of rehabilitation – an enforced 'Time Out' which gave me time to consider the good things in life and edit out the negative things that made it hard at home, at work and in my running. There was never a time that I thought I wouldn't recover and walk again, let alone run. My sixties childhood mantra of 'suck it up buttercup' meant if I gave learning to walk everything I'd got, I'd get there eventually – and I did.

For me, walking four steps unaided felt as good, and gave me the same high, as my first London Marathon, but it was considerably harder. I have total admiration for anyone that endures life wheelchair bound or suffers from any neurological illness.

Having a body that once could run hundreds of miles but then suddenly can't simply walk a step is the most frustrating and humbling thing anyone could ever experience. A real life-lesson for me.

Trinity's path and mine feel somewhat entwined and I'm honoured that she asked me to write the forward to her book. We've both struggled with relationships, addiction and run thousands of miles in races that have brought us the success that we've craved from our peers. It's a wonderful testament that she now wants to share that journey with the world.

Enjoy her story, the highs and lows, her phoenix from of the ashes climb to success and her honesty about how she's managed to create a life worth living.

Rory Coleman
Ultra-marathon Runner and Lifestyle Coach

1,150 Marathons – 270 Ultras –
15 Marathon des Sables –
9 Guinness World Records

January 2023

PART **ONE**

CHAPTER 1

A BRIEF HISTORY OF ME

I was born in Ealing, London in 1963. When I was around the age of two we moved into the London overspill new town of Stevenage in Hertfordshire. I don't ever remember feeling happy as a child, my 'home' was a hostile environment with parents who seemed to be constantly shouting and throwing things at each other or shouting at and smacking me. Once my dad even gave me the choice of "rings on or off?" when he hit me. I didn't care, it would hurt either way. I had no siblings to seek comfort from so I sought solace in my room, spending hours looking out of my window imagining a world away from where I was. It was around the age of five that I started to self-harm. I would incessantly scratch my thighs with my nails, over and over until they bled. I didn't know why I was doing what I was doing, only that it felt somehow satisfying. As I understand it now, self-harm temporarily distracts from the pain inside by creating pain on the outside. That makes perfect sense to me now remembering the confused little girl that I was.

My parents frequently separated and then after some time apart got back together. I was always left with my dad and on one particular occasion when we were going to pick up my mum, my dad told me that if I wanted my mum to come back and stay then I needed to be a good girl. As a six year old, that told me that it must be my fault that she kept leaving which led to a lifetime of me believing that I was not good enough in every way. My mum left for the final time when I was seven. A year or so later my dad started seeing the person who used to babysit me. They married when I was ten, she was twenty three and my dad was forty two. My step-mother was only interested in my dad and I always felt like I was in the way of their relationship, which created all kinds of problems, mainly for me.

It's probably no surprise that, at the age of twelve, I found that alcohol could numb the pain of life. It was common to take in lodgers in the early to mid 1970's and my step-mother's aunt and her boyfriend lodged with us for a time. He sexually abused me in the lounge of my home while my step-mother's aunt was in the kitchen. I can still see his face and feel his hand forcing my hand to touch him. I was so frightened and froze when my step-mother's aunt walked in, thinking I was going to get into trouble. Nothing was ever said of it. Two years later my step-mother's brother moved in to lodge with us. He was also a child abuser, I remember him buying me a necklace with a gold cross, impressively pulling out a £50 note from his wallet to pay for it. I took that 'gift' as a silent instruction to keep quiet about what he did when he exposed himself to me. He needn't have worried because even if I had told someone I didn't feel like anyone would believe me, I didn't feel like I mattered to anyone. A number of years later he went into the priesthood.

At the age of fifteen it felt like my life was completely out of control. I hated myself, how I looked, and everything about me. To change something I decided to lose some weight and as the weight fell off I felt like I had something to cling to in the sea of chaos. I practically stopped eating, only having just enough calories to keep me from fainting. I would pour alcohol from the drinks cabinet into little Tupperware pots and take them into school to add to my black coffee in the 6th form common room.

School friends and teachers commented on how ill and thin I looked and that attention motivated me to continue on my path to self-destruction. I had also found another life numbing substance by this time, in drugs. I became an anorexic, progressing to bulimic, alcoholic drug addict. I remember my dad once calling me a drop out so I felt that I had finally lived down to his expectations.

These were the days when there was little to no support on leaving full time education, it was a case of sink or swim. I scraped through just two 'O' Levels, and I had no idea what to do when I walked out of the school gates for the last time. My parents somehow expected me to know what I was doing without giving me any guidance and I just floundered.

My dad and step-mother decided to move down to Bournemouth with their baby son when I was around the age of nineteen. It was obvious from the start that I didn't feature in their plans so I'd have to find somewhere to live. I was frightened that I was about to become homeless so I contacted my mum and she agreed that I could have the spare room in her flat in Sandy, Bedfordshire for £25 per week (this was 1982). I saw this as a chance to have some kind of mother daughter relationship, something I'd always craved. Unfortunately my mother did not, and a series of events leading to her once again rejecting me, wound up with me in hospital having my stomach pumped after an overdose and falling into a complete nervous breakdown.

While my life was falling apart on one side, little did I realise that it was falling together in another area. This is where I start talking about running. Initially running was something I used to burn calories during bouts of anorexia and bulimia, but very slowly it became something in my life that I could hold onto and have control over, and something positive that I could add to my identity.

There was never any training plan or anything at all scientific about when, how far or how often I'd run, I'd just run and I enjoyed how it made me feel.

Alongside running, alcohol, drugs and bouts of severe depression would feature throughout my 20's, and in 1991 I almost lost my life in a drug binge but the reality of having an eighteen month old child by then gave me a massive wake up call. I wasn't going to be the absent mother that mine was. I was ready for help and I cleaned up.

CHAPTER 2

THE EARLY RACES

My first ever race was the Mansfield Half Marathon in 1981. These days there are races in almost every town in the UK but back then there were very few so I travelled from where I lived in Letchworth, Hertfordshire up to Mansfield, Leicestershire just for a half marathon. I think I finished in something like 2 hours 15 minutes but I loved the experience and was hooked from the start. I enjoyed the experience of working to achieve something and I wanted more.

The London Marathon had only just entered the race listings so I set my sights on getting a place in the 1982 race. Again it was a very different time and the London Marathon entry system has changed many times since. But as I recall, for the 1982 race you first had to get the entry form from a magazine which was only available in certain outlets. The completed form then had to be posted at one of the designated Post Offices on a certain day with a timestamp and it was basically on a first come first served system according to the time stamp.

The designated Post Office closest to me was Bedford and I, along with probably 50 or so other aspiring London Marathon runners, camped outside the Post Office overnight in just sleeping bags with flasks of tea and coffee, almost like a protest against homelessness. The Police at the time had no idea this was going to happen and were obviously confused and bemused. They didn't move us on though, thankfully and come 9am we all lined up and dutifully handed over the precious Gillette London Marathon entry form in order to be strictly time stamped. I was lucky enough to get a place in the marathon and was one of the 15,000+ finishers.

Here's a little interesting note from the London Marathon website about the 1982 race…

> *'London was already the biggest marathon in the world. Its 15,116 finishers – 198 inside 2:30:00 – put it ahead of the New York City Marathon, whose Race Director Fred Lebow was among the London runners. There was an extremely low dropout rate of just 3.6%.'*

Hugh Jones won the men's race in 2.09 and Joyce Smith won the women's race as documented here, again from the London Marathon website

> *'Joyce Smith, unchallenged as Britain's number one, again lowered her best and the UK record to 2:29:43. This time her winning margin was more than six minutes over the woman in second place, New Zealander Lorraine Moller.'*

The London Marathon is more than twice the size of that past event now, and don't quote me on this but I'm not sure it can even claim to be the biggest marathon in the world anymore, which is fantastic for both the sport and for the health of people all over the world.

Obviously the Kenyans weren't fully in the picture yet, but it wasn't going to be long before they started giving everyone a run for their money (pun intended).

I think my finish time for my first marathon was something around four and a half hours, which I remember being so disappointed with. I now know that that is a reasonably good time for a first marathon, especially as my training was at best haphazard and it was a time before running really took off so there wasn't the information on training and kit that there is now.

Having run my first half marathon and my first full marathon I suddenly became obsessed with running. But there was absolutely nothing scientific about my training, I would simply go out and run, mostly in the evenings. It was not uncommon for me to start a 20 mile run at 10pm and run through dark lanes and deserted streets without a torch or anything hi-viz about my person.

On one such occasion, late into the night, I ran into an unlit man-hole and then complained to the council. They were very apologetic and didn't even ask what I was doing running round unlit streets in the small hours.

Nothing stopped me, no, I tell a lie, only one bout of a particularly nasty flu virus, which had me bedridden for a week just after my 21st birthday, stopped me from running. I would run through injuries, mainly caused by running too much. I would also run if I was tired or not feeling too well, probably also caused by running too much. But I felt invincible most of the time.

I entered more marathons, and during the 1980's I ran twelve including four more London Marathons. By today's standards that's not many at all, but back then races were few and far between. My times ranged wildly from 4 hours and 15 minutes to almost 6 hours (Wolverhampton 1985, as I recall). I did finish one marathon in a time of 3 hours and 17 minutes, I can't remember which race it was now, but I'm not sure my fitness at that stage was up to that kind of pace so I may have taken a wrong turn, though to this day I don't know how or where, I do remember being shocked to see the finish line though. The Garmin type watch did not exist back then either. I remember it was very cold with torrential rain all day and I was practically hypothermic at the finish, unable to talk, so maybe I did put my all into the race… who knows.

My running stopped in 1988, I became pregnant with my first child in 1989 and my life as wife and mum began. I didn't run again until 2002, and it was only with the intention of getting my body back in shape after having two more children in 1993 and 1995. However, within a year I was standing at the start line of another marathon. As the saying goes, once a runner, always a runner.

CHAPTER 3

STARTING OVER

My first race back in 2002 was the Bristol half marathon, and I immediately felt just like I did at the Mansfield half marathon 21 years before. The Taunton marathon followed (4.12) and I remembered why I loved long distance running so much. I joined the Hogweed Trotters Running Club and immersed myself in training and racing. Over the next few years I ran three or four marathons a year including Taunton again, as well as marathons in Rome, Copenhagen, Majorca and in 2004 achieved that long awaited sub four hours at Cardiff marathon finishing in a time of 3.57.

While out on a long run with the club runners one Sunday, Bob Bell, the Chairman of the club at the time and a lovely gentleman who remains a good friend, talked about one of his favourite races. It was called the Dartmoor Discovery and was a 32 mile road race over the hills in Dartmoor. It sounded interesting and a good introduction into the world of ultra running. It was after all only 10 km further than a marathon so it shouldn't be too difficult.

What I failed to factor in was the size of the hills! My first experience of running the Dartmoor Discovery was in June 2004, and it was quite an experience. It was a low key and very friendly event. The race started in Princetown and the course took us through little villages with stunning scenery to wide open fairly bleak moorland with ponies and sheep roaming freely. I finished the beautifully gruelling race in a time of 6 hours and 11 minutes.

In 2005 my marriage finally ended so I focused even more on running and I returned to Devon better prepared for another attempt at the Dartmoor Discovery. I finished in 5 hours 35 minutes, winning 1st place in the LV40 age group. The experience of running further and faster felt more exciting than training and racing the same 10k, half marathon and marathon distances all the time so I entered another ultra; the Kent 50 Challenge which was actually 52.4 miles, or a double marathon. This wasn't going to be my only time running this event and I go into more detail when I recall my 2009 experience of this race but suffice to say finishing in 1st placed female with a time of 10 hours and 15 minutes on the 17th July 2005, the hottest day of the year, was very much responsible for seducing me fully into the world of ultra running. I wanted even more, further, and faster.

Training was going really well and I was enjoying my increasing pace. Marathons didn't seem that far anymore and I took ten minutes off my personal best time when I finished the Nottingham marathon in 3.47 and then just a month later I ran the Abingdon marathon in 3.40, securing a guaranteed entry at the London marathon with a GFA (Good For Age) place. Training for London started in earnest, I poured over my training schedule, entered shorter build up races to get sharp and plotted all my Sunday long runs. On April 2nd 2006 I entered the Oakley 20 mile race as a last long training run for the London marathon later in the month. At about 13 or 14 miles I felt my right leg suddenly give way for no apparent reason, but there was no pain or anything telling me to stop running so I carried on to finish in two hours and forty four minutes. But as soon as I stopped running the whole of my right leg was in intense pain. Whatever had happened in my leg at that 13/14 mile mark was about to stop me in my tracks. There would be no London marathon for me that year after all.

At the 2006 London Marathon Expo I had the painful task of returning my entry, but it meant that I could defer it for a year, by which time I was hopeful that the injury, whatever it turned out to be, would be gone and forgotten. In actual fact it proved to be a bit more complicated. I saw a number of consultants, both NHS and private, and they all had differing opinions. The scans didn't conclusively prove anything either. Eventually I was referred to a fantastic consultant who, at the end of my first consultation, promised me that he would find out the exact problem and do his best to fix it. By that time I had reams of paperwork and scan results which he asked me to give him, and he promised to do the research. I was also sent for nerve conduction studies, which was incredibly painful, but I was prepared to do anything to be able to run freely again. I have a fairly high tolerance of pain and I was still stubbornly trying to run, just short races. But I also had an entry into the Miami Marathon in January 2007 and I was not prepared to cancel my entry into that event as I had done for many others since that fateful day in Oakley. The injury didn't allow me to train properly so I decided that I would just run-walk it and enjoy the Miami experience. The Miami Marathon was an extremely painful experience, but I was so determined and made it from the start line to the finish line in 4 hours 44 minutes and 2 seconds, and 1400th place overall. A few months later I took my deferred London marathon place from the previous year and made it to the finish line in 4 hours 22 minutes and 35 seconds, so at least I was going in the right direction.

While the injury was making running marathons difficult I turned my attention to short races and competed in the Somerset Series. To be eligible to compete in the series you had to complete eight out of the sixteen mostly off-road races and the distances ranged from 5k to about 16 miles. The series challenge was all on a point scoring system on individual race placing and the objective was to finish with the lowest number of points. Even though I didn't usually like off road races, because I didn't consider myself very good on that terrain, I really enjoyed the challenge, had a lot of fun and finished the series winning 2nd placed Female. Another trophy for the cabinet.

The year of 2008 got off to a slow start due to having some spinal surgery in my neck at the end of the previous year. Plus I was still having issues with the injury in my leg and seeing my consultant regularly. I continued to have some successes at short races, the Bradley Stoke 10k being one of them when I finished 1st Female. I had also managed to get another place for the London marathon and with the help of a cortisone injection in the side of my knee I got stuck into a good training schedule. On 13th

April I finished the marathon in a very satisfying 3 hours 31 minutes and 34 seconds in 4,940th place and achieved a qualifying time to enter the Boston Marathon in the US. My last race of the year was the Amsterdam marathon on October 19th. It was a flat course and I was fairly confident that I could achieve my next goal of a sub 3.30 marathon time. All of my preparations had gone to plan and I stood confidently at the start waiting for the off. I paced the first half perfectly and felt relaxed and strong. But shortly after halfway the injury that was still hanging around after over two years sent pain shooting through my right leg. The suddenness of it caused me to feel sick and slightly light headed. The pain endorphins gradually kicked in and I pushed on. As I have previously said, I have a very high pain threshold and this was proved when I gave birth to my second child without any pain relief. She weighed 10lb 4oz at birth. Obviously the body's own pain endorphins don't always remove all pain and by the time I finished the marathon I was in total agony. I missed the sub 3.30 by only a minute, finishing in 3 hours 30 minutes and 57 seconds and surprisingly 6th in the lady vet 45 age category.

At the same time my consultant was still trying to find a way to fix the injury. He was of the opinion that the injury was to do with the Common Peroneal Nerve, which meant that it wasn't bone, joint or ligament, so that's a good thing I thought. I'd suspected that it must be a neuro problem because when it flared the pain was excruciating. It felt like the worst toothache pain ever but in the whole of my leg rather than in my mouth. My consultant was about to attend some big medical conference and was going to take my case with him in a last ditch attempt to find a solution.

I still had that ultra itch that I couldn't scratch and I needed a challenge so I decided to do something to raise funds for charity. I wanted to do something that covered a big distance but due to the injury I was obviously not able to run too far. One day while on a cross trainer at the gym trying to keep my fitness up I came up with the idea of covering 100 km on a cross trainer. It would be the challenge I craved but I didn't think it would be as tough as running it. On January 2nd 2009 I stepped on a cross trainer in a public gym and worked out for 100 km (62 miles) raising much needed funds for a charity that helps to liberate and rehabilitate bears who are made to dance in front of tourists for food. The only time I got off the machine was for trips to the 'conveniences' and the 100 km took me 13 hours, 59 minutes and 59 seconds. I can honestly say that as of this time and before the Canalslam, it's the second hardest thing I have ever done, the first being a 100 mile race but that's a whole other story that I'll write about later on.

My consultant had returned from the conference with some information and sent me for another scan. From the results of the scan he would be able to tell if it was operable or not, it turned out not. At the appointment he sat in front of me, visibly upset, and gave me the news that I didn't want to hear. He then asked me what were my main target races that I wanted to do before I would have to retire from the sport of long distance running. He said he would give me a maximum of three cortisone injections to get me through those races. My target races were one more London marathon, Boston marathon and Comrades, a 56 mile race in South Africa. My consultant appointed the best person he could find to give me the first of those three cortisone injections and I got stuck into some solid training for a big week in April. Training went very well and I was about to have an unforgettable transatlantic week. I was also tentatively looking forward to possibilities rather than entertaining any thoughts of retirement from doing what I loved.

Sometime around the middle of April 2009 I travelled to the US to run in the 113th Boston Marathon which took place on Monday April 20th. It is a marathon that every marathon runner should experience at least once. Not only is there so much history to the Boston marathon, so many great runners take part and there is such camaraderie, more than I've experienced in any other marathon, including, dare I say it, London. The marathon is such a fixture of the city that the finish line is permanently marked on the road. The Boston Marathon has a program of seminars over the marathon weekend where you can listen to inspirational talks from some of the world's greatest marathon runners. When I was there I listened to a number of running greats speak including Dick Beardsley, Team Hoyt and also Kathrine Switzer who in 1967 was the first woman to run in the Boston Marathon with an official number. Women were not actually allowed to run in marathon events back then but Kathrine was determined, she only put her initials and surname on the entry form and turned up for the race wearing a hoodie so it wasn't obvious that she was a woman. When she was spotted on the course, the race director tried to get hold of her and drag her out of the race! It's an inspirational story, and shows how far we have come in women's running even within my own lifetime.

The whole city of Boston embraces the marathon event, welcoming runners from all over the world in the lead up, supporting each and every runner before and during the race itself, and celebrating every runner's achievements for days afterward. I had an amazing race, I had prepared well and I felt confident. I ran all the way up the notorious Heartbreak Hill and pushed hard to finish in 3 hours 23 minutes and 50 seconds, a Personal Best by about eight minutes! I was 5509th out of a total of 22849 finishers, 682nd lady out of 9302, and 28th in my age category out of 1456, so not too shabby for such a big field of US and international runners. I was ecstatic to have competed in and completed this very special race, it's still my favourite marathon. After enjoying a couple of days of recovery in Boston I boarded a flight back to London, went straight to another hotel, freshened up from the long flight and then got the tube to the London Marathon expo to pick up my race number. Six days after running the Boston marathon, I ran the London Marathon in 3 hours 37 minutes and 4 seconds. Looking back at that week now, I can remember how strong I was. I felt invincible, that there was nothing I couldn't do and I believed that, even at the age of 46, I was just at the beginning of an exciting chapter in my running career.

After I'd recovered from the Boston-London double in April I ramped up my training for a return to the Dartmoor Discovery 32 mile race in early June to be followed by the Kent 50 Challenge which was on the 19th July. The weather on Dartmoor is anything but predictable so you have to be prepared for hot sunshine, freezing sleet and everything in between. This year it would be the most uncomfortable end of the spectrum. It rained at the start and just got worse. By half way the strong cold wind was pushing the icy rain horizontally causing the skin on one side of my body to become totally numb. Brave spectators and supporters were out on the course offering runners big black bin liners to put on over their kit as some protection against the harsh elements. I ran the race like I was running for cover and wanted to get it over with as soon as possible so I could get warm and dry. I finished in 4:52:45, a personal best by about 43 minutes. I was the 35th finisher, 5th lady and 3rd Lady Vet 45. There were some very strong runners ahead of me that day.

In the days before I ran the Kent 50 Challenge in 2009 a friend, now sadly passed, said to me "Best of luck for Sunday – you're in awesome form!" Those words "awesome form" stuck in my head and stayed with me through the 52.4 miles of that race. Indeed I was in great shape with PB's at every distance so far that year. I had trained really well. Not massive mileage by any means, but good solid training. I can look back now and see that what I did in 2009, the way I trained, the way I raced, the way I rested, and the way I listened to and respected what my body needed, set the foundations for the successes in ultra racing that I would have over the following years. The Kent 50 consisted of 8 x 6.55 mile laps mostly over rough cross country tracks with a short stretch of concrete and one little bump which became more like a hill and steeper with every lap. By lap 8 that little bump had somehow become a mountain to climb. There were three aid stations on the course and a lap counter at the start/finish area. There was also little if any shade and as the race was held in the middle of July, it meant that it was usually very hot throughout the day. The atmosphere was always great though, and the support was outstanding, added to that the start/finish area was at a little country pub, what could be better! I've briefly mentioned my first running of this race back in 2005, when I finished 1st Lady in a time of 10 hours 15 minutes, but now I was fitter and faster and I had more confidence in my abilities. The injury in my leg that had caused so much worry and heartache for about two years hadn't bothered me in a while, not since that expertly delivered cortisone injection in fact. I knew that there was more competition, but I felt reasonably confident of a fast time. I had a good pacing strategy that had worked really well in previous races so all I needed to do was keep my head and stick to the plan.

The first marathon went like a breeze, as did the next couple of laps, but the tiredness crept in and by the last lap everything was hurting. I tried to distract myself from how I felt by telling myself that every time I ran down a certain path or turned a certain bend or ran across a certain bit of rocky ground, that it was for the last time. It was becoming harder to keep running, but I pushed on with gritty determination. At around 48 miles I realised that I was on for under eight and a half hours so long as I kept going. My legs were feeling heavy, my feet were hurting, and my energy was running low. I remember thinking earlier in the day that I might run through the last scheduled walk break but when I got to that point at 50 miles it just wasn't an option anymore. I took a brief walk but thought of the new target time and started running again with the intention of running all the way to the finish line. I got onto the last main stretch of road before turning the bend to the finish, which was only about three quarters of a mile away. I felt dead on my feet and couldn't keep it going so I walked a bit and told myself that as soon as I saw the little white car that had been parked in the same spot all day, I would run. My body was hoping that it had moved but suddenly there it was, the target of the little white car came into view so I picked up my legs and started running, focusing on that little car all the way. I turned the bend and finally I was finished. My time of 8.27.02 was a PB by 1 hour and 48 minutes. I was exhausted and overjoyed in equal measure. As I said before, there was more competition this year so even with a much faster time than my previous attempt I just about achieved 2nd placed Female.

Six weeks later, in early September I ran in a race across Wales. It was 46 miles from Caen to Aberystwyth and the route took us over Plynlimon, the highest point in the Cambrian Mountains. It started in the dark and there was a wonderful sense of camaraderie for a good few miles. As dawn broke the runners had spread out along the Welsh hills and marshes and by the time I had reached the top of Plynlimon some time later I had lost sight of all other runners. Within minutes a heavy mist came down around me obscuring any view and I became disoriented. I almost started to panic, fearing that if I didn't get moving I could get lost up in the hills so I just started to run in a random direction, but you could call it instinctive because after a short while I felt a wave of relief when I spotted another runner in the far distance. Having been almost lost on the mountain, sunk knee deep in marshy bogs, soaking wet in sudden heavy rain and then very warm when the sun made an appearance,

I finally made it to the finish in 10 hours and 39 minutes. That was quite an adventure!

After just two weeks recovery I found myself on another start line of what was to be the next epic adventure, the London to Brighton off-road race. It was a mostly self-navigation 56 mile cross country race and because, as already established, I'm not great at navigating myself I planned on running with a friend and we set a finish target of sub 12 hours. The race started at Blackheath in the dark at 6am. I wrote about my experience just after the event and talking about the start I wrote "It was a relief to start running because then I could relax with nothing more to worry about". That describes what ultra running was to me, a time to relax and zone out. I haven't really found anything else, (apart from sleep) that does that for me to the extent that running ultras does. However, we did encounter a few issues fairly early on. There were a number of checkpoints to check in at along the course and even with my navigating buddy we got lost between the second and third checkpoints. Just as we got ourselves back on course for CP3, my buddy tripped and took a spectacular fall which resulted in spending quite some time at the checkpoint with my buddy being attended to by the medical team. With the navigational error, the accident and the consequential but necessary medical attention needed we'd lost a lot of time, and were already getting close to the later checkpoint time cut offs so we had to get moving.

It was a tough course, the hills were relentless, the terrain constantly sapped our energy and there were at least fifty stiles to climb over, which became more and more challenging with every mile particularly over the second half of the course. Added to that, due to his fall, my buddy was suffering with regular excruciatingly painful cramping in his legs and was finding it increasingly impossible to climb over the stiles so fellow runners came to his aid and lifted him over some of them. I felt bad for my buddy but it was occasionally comical to watch him with completely stiff straight legs being manoeuvred over the stile by three or four runners. There were also highlights, such as when a group of us had gone slightly off course and found ourselves on the wrong side of a barbed wire fence. While some guys held the fence down allowing those with longer legs to carefully climb over it I was figuring out how I was going to get myself over without tearing my skin on the barbed wire. Suddenly I felt myself being scooped up and lifted over. The two strong arms belonged to a rather tanned and muscular European guy who was clearly so tough that he was not even wearing any top under his backpack and from what I could see there was absolutely no chafing either, just rather pert nipples and deliciously ripped abs. It sounds like a dream but yes, it actually did happen!

So back to the race, by the time we got to the forth and penultimate checkpoint we were chasing the clock and had been forced to adjust our target time to make it to the finish line before the 13 hour cut off. My buddy's bandages were seeping blood and his legs were still constantly cramping whilst he was bravely trying to run. I was very aware of the time slipping away and had to urge him to keep going through the pain. As we left the fifth and final checkpoint with over forty miles behind us we could see Blackcap, the final climb, ahead. We made it to the top and I was on a runner's high, but it didn't last long because as we got close to the fifty six mile point, at which the race distance should have been covered or close to, I still couldn't see any sign of the finish at all. I asked my buddy to look at the map and tell me how far he thought we had to go. To keep me reasonably positive he lied and told me that it was about a mile and a half. It turned out to be about three and a half miles and just before we saw the arrows to the finish I was struggling to hold it together both mentally and emotionally. We had to run the last few hundred yards to the finish line over pebbles which accentuated our now very unstable legs. My buddy wanted to walk but I told him he couldn't because we had started together, ran together and we were going to finish together plus, selfishly I desperately needed it all to be over. We ran through the finish, I stumbled over to the side, collapsed onto the ground and could do nothing else but cry. The whole event had demanded so much of me physically, mentally and emotionally, I was exhausted and empty. That is also what ultra running is all about for me, pushing the limits of what I think my body can do.

244 runners started the race. We were 130th and 131st out of 157 official finishers finishing inside the 13 hour cut off. We did it with just 10 minutes to spare having covered 59.8 miles.

My good friend and the running club Chairman Bob, who had lured me into ultra running with the Dartmoor Discovery, had also mentioned another race that he thought I might want to consider. He told me about the Comrades Marathon in South Africa. As soon as I read about it on the internet I felt that familiar butterflies in the belly excitement and decided that I would one day run that race. Despite it being called a marathon, the race distance is actually about

56 miles and over some very big hills. You have to qualify to gain entry to this race and in September 2009 I decided I was ready and put my application in, which was then accepted conditional to running a qualifying time.

The year 2010 got off to a great racing start with Gloucester marathon on January 24th in a time of 3 hours 29 minutes, the Duchy marathon in Cornwall on 7th March in 3 hours 26 minutes, and the Great Welsh Marathon on 18th April where I pushed myself to 3 hours and 25 minutes and 2nd placed Female, having been leading the ladies race up until about half way. It was a two lap course and as I went through half way to start the second lap, over the speaker the race announcer said my name and that I was in first place but being chased down by the second place runner. I let those words get into my head and then the pressure got to me. All credit to the lady who chased me down though.

More importantly I had my qualifying time, and I was looking forward to the challenge of Comrades in June. I regularly ran hill repeats trying to prepare myself for the long steep climbs in South Africa. My last 'training' marathon was the North Dorset Village marathon where I took it easy to avoid injury and finished in 3 hours and 40 minutes. I then had just two more races before Comrades to sharpen up my speed, a half marathon in Tewkesbury, Gloucestershire where I finished in 91 minutes 33 seconds, and a 10km race organised by my club called the Hogweed Trot where I ran a time of 41.27. Knowing I could run these times gave me more confidence and I had my eye on a sub 3.15 at the Berlin marathon in September which would qualify me for a London Marathon Championship entry. These were really exciting times, I could actually tell myself that I was reasonably good at something and that I wasn't the drop out that my father told me I was.

There is so much that I could say about Comrades but whatever I say could not even begin to describe how special the event is. Just as I believe that every marathon runner should experience Boston, every ultra distance runner should experience Comrades. Just like the Boston Marathon, there is a long and fascinating history to Comrades. The race itself alternates each year between an 'up run' and a 'down run', the up run starts in Durban and finishes in Pietermaritzburg, and vice versa, but don't think the down run is any easier! My first Comrades was a down run and the pain that the long steep downhills inflicted on my quads in the second half had me literally crying out in agony. There are different medals depending on what time you finish the race in, starting from gold for the first ten finishers, and the Wally Hayward Medal for those who do not finish within the top 10 but who dip under 6 hours. Then there's the Isavel Roche-Kelly medal for women only who finish outside of the top 10 but under the 7.30 mark. A silver for those finishing under 7 hours 30 minutes, the Bill Rowan medal for those finishing under 9 hours, then bronze for under 11 hours and finally the Vic Clapham medal for 12 hours and under. Anyone finishing from 12 hours and 1 second onwards doesn't get an official finish time or a medal. Yes, that may sound harsh, but that's the challenge and everyone who enters the race accepts that challenge.

The race starts at 5.30am. It's freezing cold and as dark as night. There is a ritual of songs and an anthem before the start of the race which heightens the excitement. I remember standing in the pen surrounded by fellow

Comrades runners and thinking to myself, I'm actually here, I'm actually realising one of my dreams right here right now! Finally, on the sound of a cockerel the race is on. There had been warnings of the raised cats-eyes in the middle of the road, but just a couple of kilometres into the race I still managed to catch one with the tip of my shoe and I went flying, landing and sliding painfully on the tarmac. With my knee and hands grazed and bleeding I picked myself up and carried on as fellow runners asked me if I was okay. The sunrise started to warm the air and it wasn't long before it felt very warm. By midday the African sun was sapping my strength and added to that, I had another issue in the form of a severe allergic reaction to the all-day sun cream that I'd used the day before. My arms and legs were swollen and with the heat had become unbearably itchy. Big target races don't always go to plan, but I was certainly having a very different day to what I had anticipated.

I had my sights set on a Bill Rowan medal, named after the very first winner of Comrades who finished in just under 9 hours. There are pacing groups in Comrades that they call 'busses' and there were two busses for the sub 9 hour finish. For the first half of the race I was ahead of both but as I slowed I could hear one of them getting closer. It's an awesome sound, almost like the steady marching of a huge army all in time. As the bus scooped me up I decided to stay with it but I was gradually moved to the back. I held on as long as I could until I fell out the back and then watched the bus disappear off into the distance. The second sub 9 hour bus wasn't far behind and I made another attempt at staying with this one. But as I was once again spat out the back I knew then that I wouldn't be receiving the Bill

Rowan medal. I finished my first Comrades in 9:14:12. I was still ecstatic to have finished such an iconic event but a little disappointed in missing my target time so I decided that I would have to go back and try again the following year. More training was needed, and a different sun cream!

A month after running 56 miles in South Africa I showed up for a local 5k race. What I hate about racing a 5k is that it's pure pain from the B of the bang to the finish line. The lungs crave more and more oxygen as the body is forced to work harder and harder. Trying to suck in the air when pushing that hard almost feels like suffocating. But thankfully it is over relatively quickly. I finished the 5k in 20:02, which was only three seconds off a target I'd set myself in order that I could retire from that race distance forever. It would be less than a year until I could tick that particular box. The following month I went back to Kent for a final run of the 50 Challenge. I finished in 8 hours and 12 minutes, once again placing 2nd Lady and a full two hours faster than my first attempt five years previously. Incidentally, the first lady this year won it in something like seven and a half hours! It was wonderful to see so many women moving up in ultra distance running, especially as women have only been allowed to run in marathon events since the early 1970's.

Now the race was on to get the long slow ultras out of my legs and train for a quick marathon at Berlin in September. I had endurance so my training focused on speed work and hill reps for strength. I raced a 10k (41:13) and a 5 mile race (33:50) on consecutive days in August, followed up with a couple of reasonably quick long runs and a short taper and I was ready. It was a cold wet day in Berlin on the 26th September 2010. This was going to be a serious attempt at the much longed for sub 3.15 marathon time which would then qualify me for a Championship place at the London marathon. I tucked in with the sub 3:15 pace group and felt comfortable in the early miles. But as we got further into the race it felt a little too quick, and it was. I was checking the splits on my watch and could see that it was ten to fifteen seconds per mile quicker than the 3:15 pace but at the time I didn't feel confident enough to leave the group and pace myself so I hung on. At about 17.5 miles I suddenly felt like I was running through treacle. I can still remember that moment desperately trying to will my legs to move quicker. The 3.15 pace group was slowly pulling away from me and I couldn't stay with them but through gritted teeth I pushed as hard as I possibly could. At 25 miles I was suddenly in intense pain as my right calf seized up with cramp. I had no alternative but to stop and stretch it out but I quickly got back on the course and ran like my life depended on it. I ran through the Brandenburg Gate and crossed the finish line in 3 hours 19 minutes 51 seconds, relieved but bitterly disappointed. The early pace that had been too fast almost definitely cost me the five extra minutes in the second half of the race.

If I had been able to see into the future and know that my running days and races were about to be numbered I would have felt gratitude and elation at the end of a fantastic marathon achievement, not disappointment. Missing a goal finish time by five minutes means nothing when you cannot run at all. I ran two further marathons that year, Abingdon (3.26) and the Cornish marathon (3.42). I put the disappointments behind me, focused on my achievements and looked forward to the races already in the calendar for 2011.

CHAPTER 4

ULTRARACE SERIES CHAMPIONSHIP, COMRADES & A 100 MILE RACE

In training for Comrades 2011 I knew that I needed to incorporate some longer distance races, that's when I discovered the ULTRArace series organised by Rory Coleman. The first two were the Ur 45/90 on the 22nd and 23rd January 2011. This was a 45 mile race alongside the Grand Union Canal from Northampton to Tring on the Saturday and then all the way back again along the same route on Sunday. The daily mileage didn't really worry me, I was fairly confident that I could run 45 miles, but I'd never attempted a back to back ultra before so it was going to be new ground for me on the run back on Sunday. It was a cold January day and the canal towpath was muddy and rutted in places making it difficult to run so I was very happy to have completed day one not only in a respectable time of seven hours and forty five minutes, but also finishing placed 3rd female. Cold, wet and muddy I checked into the hotel and ran a cold bath to ease the trauma on the muscles in my legs. After shivering for twenty minutes in a cold bath and then having a short warm shower to avoid becoming hypothermic I ordered a carb heavy room service meal and ate as much as I could stomach. I then set the alarm for early, and slept. The next morning I briefly questioned my sanity as I got ready, pinned my number on and prepared my pack but I got myself on the start line for the run home. The first running steps felt like I was running on a trampoline and not going anywhere. My legs were sore and complaining but after a mile or two they surrendered and I was back in my stride. Less people started and even less finished the second day. But those who did were clearly the hard core and I was slightly further back in that field finishing 4th female in a time of eight hours and thirty four minutes. So my cumulative time for the ninety miles was sixteen hours and nineteen minutes and overall 3rd female.

Having completed my first back to back ultra in January I decided to enter another. The ULTRArace Grantham races were alongside more canals, taking place on the 5th and 6th of March 2011, with distances only just making it into the 'ultra' category with a 29.3 mile run out and then all the way back the next day. The one thing about running so many races back then is that I don't always remember the courses or even the race itself sometimes, just snapshot memories of which were always good. I finished day one in eleventh place out of 115 finishers, in a time of four hours and twelve minutes and placed 1st female! On day two I once again came in to finish eleventh place but out of a smaller field of 84 finishers. My time was four hours and nineteen minutes which was enough to get me 1st female for the second time that weekend. This was a good indication of where my fitness was for Comrades. The Grantham double was 58.6 miles mostly off-road canal path and my cumulative time was eight hours and thirty one minutes. Comrades was 56 miles all on road and I was targeting eight hours and fifty five minutes. All I needed to do was build some hill strength into my legs and stay injury free. As well as some slower ultras and quickish marathons I was doing specific hill training up and down the same hill between ten and fifteen times and I would do that session two or three times a week, every week. When I wasn't doing that I would run some local hilly routes. I wasn't going to be beaten at Comrades this year! So after months of hard training and a good taper I felt that I had done all that I could to achieve my goal. I arrived in South Africa feeling quietly confident, and as a post-race treat I had booked myself on a Safari trip in Kruger National Park.

At 5am on the 29th May I stood shivering at the start line of the Comrades 'Up Run' in Durban, about to run 56 miles of steep hills to finish in Pietermaritzburg. Just like the previous year, I felt very emotional during the ritual of songs and anthem in the few minutes before finally the sound of the cockerel indicated the start of the race. I don't remember too much of the race itself, other than feeling strong as I ran up the seemingly endless hills. The support along the course is incredible, it's almost as loud as the support at the London marathon in places. Hundreds and hundreds of people come out to cheer the runners on, handing out sweets, fruit, biscuits, and water to the ever grateful runners as the energy sapping heat bears down on us. In the second half of the race I was going strong and still on target for the magical sub 9 hours. When my Garmin watch battery died it was almost a relief because as I became more tired, calculating time splits to make sure I was still on target became as difficult as a question on quantum physics. Now there were no numbers to look at on my watch, I didn't have to think about it. I did occasionally ask other runners how much time we had before the 9 hour cut off and they all said that it was fine and we were going to make it. As I got closer I found more energy from somewhere and picked my feet up and ran hard for the finish line. I saw the clock in the distance and could have cried. I crossed the line in eight hours fifty minutes eighteen seconds. I was overjoyed, all the hard work had paid off. It was a massive improvement on the previous year, and I had finally achieved that coveted Bill Rowan medal! I was also awarded a Back-to-Back medal which is given to those who finish consecutive Comrades races. I was so happy! I simply can't put into words how awesome it is to run Comrades, it is an experience I will carry with me always and I feel so grateful to have achieved that dream.

Just under four weeks later, still on a high from my experience in South Africa, I was about to attempt my first 100 mile race. It was the Cotswold 100 and another event in the ULTRArace series. The race started at Stratford-upon-Avon on June 24th and the course took us south through lovely Cotswold towns and villages before looping round and heading up through more beautiful little towns and villages to the finish where we started in Stratford-upon-Avon. The furthest I'd run in one go by that time was sixty miles, and of course I'd run the 45/90 but as I was to find out, it's a very different thing to run sixty miles in one go or indeed ninety miles over a weekend with a meal and a good sleep in the middle than it is to run a 100 mile race straight. I naively believed that I could run it on my ultra race experience thus far, I had not put serious thought into a pacing strategy or planned my race day nutrition in the detail needed for this distance and consequently I suffered badly. By thirty miles in I started to feel nauseous, by forty miles in I couldn't keep anything down and even water was making me feel sick. At the fifty mile check point, having not been able to eat or drink hardly anything for twenty miles I ended my race with a DNF (Did Not Finish). I took the lessons that I'd learnt and put the experience behind me.

About another six weeks on, in August 2011 I travelled to the island of Jersey for a race called 'Round The Rock'. This was a forty six mile race which followed the coastal path up and down and all the way around the island. As I've mentioned before I was never a lover of off-road races so I don't know why I kept entering them, but I did really enjoy this one despite taking some spectacular falls leaving me with scars on my knee and elbows that will be lifelong reminders of that fun day in Jersey. I finished the race in eight hours forty seven minutes. I was 26th out of a total of 96 finishers and 6th female. It was a great day!

My fifth event in the Ur series was a couple of weeks later on 21st August. It was the ULTRArace Peaks 40 mile race in Derbyshire and as the name suggests, it had some big hills but the scenery was definitely worth the effort plus I was surrounded by good friends having as much fun as

I was, what could be better! Finishing my fifth race meant I had now run the required amount of races to be in the Championship.

My last two races of the year were in Nottingham. On 11/9/11 I went back to the Robin Hood marathon where in 2005 I was overjoyed to finish with a 10 minute PB of 3 hours 47. I'd improved so much over those six years that I finished very comfortably a full twenty minutes faster. I could definitely have raced a quicker time but my main focus was on the ULTRArace Championship and I wanted to be recovered enough to compete in the final race in the 2011 series. This was the CityULTRA 50 km in Nottingham which took place on the 9th October. I knew that to win the Championship I had to finish 2nd or above in the female race. Though there are never any guarantees in ultra running I felt reasonably confident at the start line and I decided that I was going to go out and enjoy the last race of what had been a great series of events. At 40km with just 10km to go I knew I had it in the bag. I finished in a time of 4:23:31, 15th overall and 2nd female. The Championship presentation took place after that last race in Nottingham, and it was a fantastic way to end my competitive racing for the year with some good friends and a cold beer. I'd enjoyed the competition so much and was already planning to defend my ULTRArace Ladies title in 2012.

As the previous year the first Championship races of 2012 were the Ur 45/90. So on the third weekend of bitterly cold January it was back to Northampton for a forty five mile run along the Grand Union Canal towpath to Tring. Then getting clean, warm, dry, fed and rested in a hotel before the run back along the same course the following day.

Comparing the results between the two years shows that my fitness was fairly stable, but also where you place in a race is usually about who shows up and in 2012 I got lucky.

2011
Day 1: 21st place overall, 3rd female, 7 hours 45 minutes
Day 2: 13th place overall, 4th female, 8 hours 34 minutes
Weekend placing: 3rd female, 16 hours 19 minutes

2012
Day 1: 10th place overall, 1st female, 7 hours 34 minutes
Day 2: 16th place overall, 1st female, 8 hours 49 minutes
Weekend placing: 1st female, 16 hours 23 minutes.

Next on the race schedule was the ULTRArace London Ultra 50 km in February. I didn't run this one in 2011 and didn't know the course. It was an off road race from Grove Park near Mottingham, through SE London, Crystal Palace, Streatham Common, Wandsworth, Wimbledon, Richmond Park onto Perivale finishing on a running track. Almost 200 runners were entered with some great competition so I was having to push pretty hard to stay in a reasonable position. Myself and three other girls constantly jostled for 2nd and 3rd positions. I got myself into 2nd position and all was going okay until I suddenly realised with about five or six kilometres to go that I was off course and there were no other runners around me. I must have missed a turning somewhere and by the time

I worked out where I had gone wrong and got back on to the route again I suspected that I had lost any hope of a place on the podium. Then I heard a girl behind me and at a quick glance I recognised her from the others I had been running with, which told me that maybe I could still get 3rd place if I stayed ahead of her. She pushed pretty hard and made it a very tough race but I gave it my all and finished 3rd female in a time of 4:57:11, 4th female was just thirty seven seconds behind me!

In March 2012 it was time for me to revisit the challenge of the 100 mile race and this time it was the Thames Path 100, an event organised by Centurion Running. The race started on Saturday 3rd March 2012 and meanders along the Thames from Richmond in South West London to the centre of Oxford. It was one of those days with four seasons of weather in 24 hours. We had sunshine, rain, warmth, cold, hail, wind and stillness. I had learnt a lot from my previous attempt at the distance the year before and unlike the last time, I had a plan. I had a pacing strategy and a nutrition plan of what I would need to eat and drink at certain stages in order to keep my energy levels and hydration where it needed to be to give me the best chance to complete the challenge. Obviously you can't do this kind of distance without a good support team, well some can but I wasn't in that kind of league so I arranged for a crew from about half way to support me through the night. When I arrived at the halfway crew point to find that my night support crew were not there I started to panic. But a good friend, Dave Fawkner, offered to share his team and I gratefully accepted. They were fantastic and I know I would definitely not have made it to the finish if it wasn't for their constant support and motivation. I'm not going to write about this event in detail because the finite details of all the races is not what I want this book to be about, but I'll run through some of the highlights, and low-lights that I remember. Although I loved running, there are times in any race, particularly the longer ones, where I could feel quite low and sometimes just getting through those patches was, and still is a challenge in itself. I remember having one of those times during the race and when I took my eyes off the ground two feet ahead of me I looked up and saw the most beautiful rainbow which gave me a huge lift out of my darkness and put my mind in a better place. Going off course is always really annoying but especially when the course is already a long way. Dave and I were running along and chatting casually and then we saw quite a few runners on the other side of the river, added to that there was also a fence between us and them. So we had no choice but to turn around and back track, frustratingly adding three extra miles. Running through the night on tired legs in the cold, let's face it, can be very tough, especially for the relatively inexperienced, as I was then. But the real difficulty came when it was time to leave an aid station that was inside a nice warm building with lovely people giving out hot food and hot drinks. To get up, go outside and start running again in the cold, dark night in the rain when all I wanted to do was sleep in the warm was a tough challenge all of itself. That's the point where I had to remind myself that no one was making me do this, it was a challenge that I had taken on to test my own limits. The rain was relentless, we were soaked to the skin and so cold but we kept trudging forward. Dave and I worked well together, when he was low I would urge him along and vice versa. Running on thick slippery wet mud was becoming an increasingly impossible task. Dave's support team were now running alongside us and knew exactly how much further it was to the finish and told us in the number of bridges we had left to cross. They urged us on saying things like "Only five more bridges to go". But five bridges came and went and there were still more, "Just one more bridge" they would say but would repeat that over and over until Dave and I started to lose hope. Naturally we became a little bit tetchy at the time but it remains a long running joke to this day.

Through the gusting wind and sheets of rain I could just make out the vague outline of the Finish Line. We'd made it, and just in time because the conditions were so bad that the organisers had started to take runners off the course for health and safety reasons, and a high risk of tired runners becoming hypothermic. This was a harsh reality for some, who'd even made it to the 95 mile check point when the course had to be closed, but the safety of runners was and is paramount and by that stage it could take anything up to two hours to cover the last five miles. I believe those who were unable to finish due to the course closure were given a free entry the following year. Some competitors finished the same day, and we probably would have too if it wasn't for the three extra miles that we added earlier in the day. Dave and I crossed the finish line together in 24 hours and 44 minutes. The following day I boarded a flight to New Zealand to spend a few weeks with my partner (who would later become my husband). A twenty three hour flight followed by a couple of weeks of trekking in the South Island was probably not the best way to recover from a 100 mile race, but I was in a fairly new relationship and clearly keen to impress.

Returning to the UK, and to my focus on the ULTRArace series, my fourth race was a distance of fifty miles over the Brecon Beacons in Wales. One hundred and twenty five runners finished and I was 17th overall and 2nd female finishing in eight hours and twenty minutes. I needed just one more race to qualify for my Championship entry so for this I returned to one of my favourite races in the series, the ULTRArace Peaks in Derbyshire. Of the 59 finishers only 6 were women and I finished the forty miles in twentieth place overall and 1st female in seven hours and forty six seconds, which also secured my first place in the ladies ULTRArace Championship. With that in the bag I decided to volunteer to be on the other side for the last race of the championship, and had some fun marshalling at one of the aid stations at the City Ultra in Nottingham before receiving my prize at the final presentation. Sadly that was the last year of the ULTRArace Championship, so I'm really happy to have had the opportunity to experience some great individual races within a superbly organised event, and made lifelong friends. Plus of course, I retained my title.

Apart from the ULTRArace Championship I raced four and a half more marathons and finished two more independent ultras in that year. On the 14th January was the Country to Capital 43 mile race from Wendover, near Aylesbury, to Little Venice in London, where I finished 2nd female, beaten to 1st place by just thirty seconds. The race was organised by Go Beyond Ultra and the race report they published following the race made it sound more exciting than I was aware of at the time. Here is the excerpt on the ladies race,

> '*The ladies race was an even closer affair* [than the men's] *with only 2 minutes separating the leading 3 at the finish. The early pace was set by Claire Shelley who built a 5 minute lead over the first 8 miles which she maintained over the rolling countryside of the first half. Cath Holloway in second started to close the gap once the runners reached the canal and moved into the lead shortly before thirty miles. Behind them Trinity Booth, Sandra Bowes and Wendy Shaw were vying for third place some 13 minutes behind the lead. By the 32 mile mark these 3 had caught Claire and were making serious inroads into the race leader. The four pursuing ladies were within a minute of each other and had closed the deficit to Cath to just 6 minutes. Wendy Shaw was the first to make a move getting within sight of the leader at the final checkpoint before falling back to third place. Trinity Booth finished strongly to claim second place in 6 hours 50 minutes but the winning lady on the day was Cath Holloway in 6:49:30, also claiming the Female Vet prize in the process.*'

Then on the 1st April, a few days after returning from New Zealand, I was in Ireland on the start line of the Connemara Ultra. I ran/walked my jetlagged body 39 miles to the finish in six hours and fifty one minutes so at least I had plenty of time to take in the beautiful scenery! I also attempted the Grand Union Canal 145 mile race in June but had to DNF. I dropped out at 85 miles, mainly due to breaking my glasses and then having difficulty seeing, which can be particularly hazardous when running beside a canal in the dark. I wouldn't be back for another attempt until ten years later, after very much water under the bridge and some major life changes.

Twenty twelve was another satisfying year of racing but little did I know then that a perfect storm was brewing which would be a prelude to changing my life forever.

PART **TWO**

CHAPTER 5

2013 THE PERFECT STORM

The year 2013 started off with the challenge of running four marathons in four days. The event is called the Enigma Quadzilla and one of many events organised by a good friend, David "Foxy" Bayley. Each marathon consisted of seven and a bit laps of a lake in Milton Keynes. The Enigma races are always very social events and a great place to catch up with good friends from the running community on and off the course. I'd not run this many marathons over consecutive days before and didn't really know what to expect. I was reasonably confident in running the first two but I didn't know how my body was going to hold up over day three and then day four. So on day one I ran conservatively and finished quite comfortably in three hours fifty eight minutes. Day two was another comfortable run and I was surprised to finish a few minutes faster in three hours fifty five minutes. At a third start line in as many days I was in new territory and consequently slower, finishing in four hours and seven minutes. Finally day four and a surprising result. I somehow ran the fastest of the four marathons on the last day with a finish time of 3:54:56! It felt like a good strong start to another year of racing and I was looking forward to running some great events to mark the year I turned 50 years of age.

To celebrate my actual fiftieth birthday in March, Paul and I went to Barcelona for a long weekend. I love Barcelona, it's probably my favourite Spanish city. For me there is something about the whole feel of the city and the hospitality of the Catalan people is so welcoming. Of course it was the weekend of the marathon and of course I included it in the itinerary. I ran the Barcelona marathon in a time of three hours and twenty nine minutes. Four weeks later, I was at the start line of another 26.2 mile race. The Sussex marathon was two laps of a hilly course with the halfway point, and therefore also the run to the finish, going straight uphill. This was one of the toughest marathons in the UK which is reflected in the finish times. The first male finisher crossed the line in two hours and fifty two minutes, the first female in three hours and thirty seven minutes. I was third female and finished in three hours and fifty two minutes.

The Milton Keynes marathon was next on the list, but I wasn't racing this one, I had been asked to be an official pacer. I had paced before, mostly half marathons and I really enjoyed the experience of helping others achieve their goals. I felt honoured to have been asked and obviously confident in the task ahead. Wearing my bright orange official pacer shirt and surrounded by a big group of runners, the race started well. As the miles ticked over I was running comfortably, chatting to some of the runners around me and keeping a steady pace. Then out of nowhere my lungs felt tight. We were only about six miles from the finish so I pushed on. But within a mile I was struggling to breathe, and collapsed gasping for breath. The pace group had to go on without me and I desperately hoped that at least one of them would take over and get them all to the line. Almost immediately I was surrounded by medics and taken to hospital in an ambulance with blue lights and sirens. I feared it was an asthma attack, as having exercise induced asthma I had experienced asthma attacks before and this felt the same, but the paramedics tested my oxygen levels and they weren't low enough for it to be asthma related. Tests at the hospital didn't reveal anything conclusive either, so I was eventually sent home and told to rest.

I was still not feeling well a week or so later so I saw my own GP and he arranged a number of blood tests. At the follow up appointment with my GP he told me that the blood tests revealed that I'd had Glandular Fever in the past six to eight weeks, and that I should take it easy for a few more weeks. My GP was aware that I was a long distance runner so probably should have been a little more precise about how much time I should rest, but I took him at his word and was running again a few weeks later and on the 29th June I was in a race running up mountains in the Pyrenees which took us to the top of Canigou (2,785 metres). The event was much more technical than I had anticipated, and as mountain climbing is not something I am any good at or indeed enjoy, I pulled out of the race at 42km. It had taken me over nine hours to get to marathon point and I was not going to get to the next checkpoint before the time cut off, and besides I'd had enough. I couldn't face another kilometre, let alone the remaining 25 kilometres to the finish. I was not having fun or enjoying the day at all and there was nothing in me that wanted to continue to the finish. Maybe this was not the mind-set of the ultra runner that I was but like I say, the storm was coming and my body was trying to tell me something.

Around the same time I was having some deep concerns about my 19 year old daughter. The subject of which is not something I want to, or can write about right now but suffice to say I began to suffer with anxiety and have frequent panic attacks. Looking back at 2013, all the signs were there for what was to come because one morning in September I woke up feeling like I'd been hit by a bus overnight. My whole body hurt and for no apparent reason. I actually wrote in a Facebook post the following, "Which is better… a very short two or three day virus that comes in like a freight train and knocks you flat out to the point where you start thinking about what songs you'd like to be played at your funeral and feeling so tired but at the same time frightened to sleep because you just know that you're not going to wake up again, or a long and rather annoying virus that creeps up, niggles for a while, pretends to go but stays hanging around for weeks?" The consensus was the short sharp one, but what I had was definitely not going to be short term. I had clearly put my malaise down to a random bug and carried on as normally as I could. Little did I know how sick my body actually was.

In October I had an entry into the Cricklade half marathon and at about twelve miles into the race I just stopped. There was no real reason, I felt ok, I wasn't injured, and I still had plenty of energy, I just didn't want to run anymore so I sat down on the grass verge and thought about what to do. I came to the conclusion that I didn't want to concern the race marshals for no real reason so I got up and ran to the finish. Again, this was my body trying to tell me to stop and listen. However, even with the unexplained stop I finished the race in 96 minutes.

Later that month I had to have travel vaccinations to go to Nepal, and in November Paul and I took part in the Everest marathon. This involved a two week trek up to base camp at Gorak Shep at an altitude of 5,164 metres and then running the marathon which undulated over rough trails, some of it quite technical, but overall descending about 1,700 metres to the finish at Namche Bazaar. On the trek up, a few days before we were to arrive at Gorak Shep I experienced some altitude sickness. I had a headache, more breathless than usual and also some confusion so the medics that travelled with us prescribed Diamox and after an extra rest day I was able to continue climbing and re-join the group. Some competitors were not so fortunate and had to be airlifted down. It was certainly a once in a lifetime trip for me and not too many people can say they've run a marathon from Everest Base Camp. We mostly camped overnight during the trek and it was very common, not just for me but for many others in the group to wake up in the middle of the night suddenly gasping for breath due to the reduced oxygen at altitude.

At the start line of the Everest Marathon it was minus fifteen degrees centigrade and the first few miles were a scramble over rocks and ice. The course continued over very technical trail, overall descending but with some big climbs as well. I'm not what you'd call a natural trail runner and was running with Paul who, although was slightly stronger than me on the trail, I knew we were towards the back end of the field. When at one point I turned around and saw the 'race sweepers' I realised that we weren't *towards* the back, we were *actually at* the back of the race. I mentioned this to Paul and he was as surprised as me. Now with some urgency we moved up through the field and eventually finished in 9 hours and 43 minutes, and nowhere near last.

While this event was an amazing experience, the three week trip put a huge amount of stress on my body. In normal circumstances physical stress was something I was used to and would recover from quite quickly, but with all of the other stresses, the family trauma, the anxiety and panic attacks, the vaccinations to travel and previous long distance runs pushing my body to physical limits, all on top of having Glandular Fever, which as I was to discover needed more than a just few of weeks of rest to recover from, my body was broken and I was about to find out how broken it was. My final race of the year was back in Milton Keynes, around the same course as the Quadzilla which I ran at the beginning of the year. This time it was just the one 26.2 mile marathon but within six miles I was finished, I could not run, and I didn't know why. Something was very wrong.

At the same time my business Top2Toe Fitness was going from strength to strength and I was so busy with clients that I asked Paul if he would like to join me in the business. I didn't have to ask twice because he was keen to get involved and immediately looked for Personal Trainer courses and signed up. The plan was that after he'd passed his course he would assist me for a period of time to settle in before taking on new clients of his own. The universe had a different plan.

CHAPTER 6

2014

Whilst I was still working I had taken some time off running in the belief that a good rest for about six weeks was all I needed. I tentatively returned to training in late January of 2014. Initially I was hopeful but at the end of one particular run of around six or seven miles I suddenly felt very unwell. I had less than a mile left of my run but had to call in on a friend to ask if she could drive me home. I couldn't understand what was wrong or why running kept making me ill. I had a reasonably physical job working as a Personal Trainer with my own thriving business and living a reasonably normal life, but if I ran I became ill. I stubbornly kept trying to run but when a short three mile run floored me again I knew that I would have to seek medical answers. A full range of blood tests did not reveal anything and after a number of appointments with my GP I was still no further forward in finding out what was wrong with me.

During this time I had been getting progressively worse and not only could I not run at all I was also finding it difficult to walk very far. Even holding a normal conversation became frustratingly difficult. My brain seemed to stop working and I couldn't find the simplest of words causing even short conversations to become impossible. I couldn't think with any sense of clarity and began to lose confidence in myself so I avoided conversation when possible. All this was taking its toll on my mental health and Paul arranged a mini break for us in France over my birthday, but I was constantly crashing with any amount of activity. When we returned home I admitted defeat and on the 25th March I had to stop working. By this time Paul had completed his courses and was a fully qualified Personal Trainer but there would be no 'settling in' period as previously planned, he would have to go straight in at the deep end and take over training all of my clients. I sat in on a few of the sessions but even that, just sitting and concentrating on what Paul was teaching exhausted me. He appeared to be doing just fine and our clients were happy so I left him to it.

Meanwhile I'd had test after test for all kinds of illnesses but the results all came back negative. With the NHS doctors admitting that they could not find anything I went to a private doctor. Another full range of tests were done and when they all came back negative it was then that I was diagnosed with Myalgia Encephalomyelitis (ME). There is currently no test for ME although now there is 'Long Covid' which has very similar symptoms and the medical profession has taken more of an interest in this which in turn could benefit those with ME. It's a shame that it had to take a relatively new illness to offer any kind of hope to people with ME who have already been suffering for many many years. However at the moment it's still the case that

ME can only be diagnosed by ruling everything else out. Obviously this can and does take a very long time and by the time I had the diagnosis I was practically bedridden. I was in so much pain and in a constant state of fatigue, and when I did get out of bed it would take me a painfully long time to get down the stairs, one agonising step after another hanging on to the handrail as if my life depended on it. Just the act of getting out of bed and down the stairs took all the strength and energy I had and would leave me exhausted.

It felt like my life was being taken away from under me and the more I searched for information on the condition I'd been diagnosed with, the worse I felt. There appeared to be no hope of recovery from ME, there were only suggestions and advice on how to adapt your life to the illness and live with it. With all the negative information filling my head it wasn't long before I found myself slipping into a hopeless depression.

Even when Paul proposed to me in a very romantic setting I hesitated to accept, not because I didn't want to be married to him, I just didn't want to be a burdensome sick person, holding Paul back from the life adventures that I knew he enjoyed so much. But I did accept his proposal and almost immediately started planning our wedding.

While planning our wedding distracted my mind from my situation, it was also very exhausting. The brain fog made thinking a challenge in itself and that along with the pain in my joints and muscles meant that I couldn't concentrate on something for very long. I do have a well hidden creative streak and had decided to make our own wedding invitations, and also to decorate a keepsake box for the guests to post little messages on post-it notes into. On the 29th June my Facebook post read "I'm exhausted and aching all over, exactly like I used to feel on Sunday afternoons. Back then it was due to running lots of miles over big hills, today it is due to less than an hour of decoupage". I did try to keep some humour but consistent resting from small activities like this was essential and it frustrated the hell out of me.

Here started a period of my life that when I look back I find myself not liking that person very much. I let self-pity in and that took me away from my friends. Most of my friends were runners and I couldn't bear to see the posts on Facebook about running and races so I'm ashamed to say that I took a lot of friends out of my Facebook friends list, not because of anything they had said or done, or because I didn't want to have them as a friend, it was just so painful knowing that I didn't belong in the running community anymore. Obviously not everyone knew that I was sick and would invite me to races or ask which race I had coming up. They were my friends and were interested in me but I would respond to posts like that with a barrel full of self-pity and a hint of resentment at the world at large. I took myself away from the running community, from my friends who cared about me and from life outside. My constant state of confusion with the brain fog meant that I couldn't make quick decisions and certainly not the sort of reflex decisions that you sometimes need when behind the wheel, so I stopped driving for the safety of myself and others, for the following eighteen months.

I watched my clients turn up at our studio to be trained by Paul, I watched them leave and then another turn up.

I missed being the Personal Trainer, I missed my clients, I missed watching them improve and witnessing them feeling good about themselves. I felt angry, resentful, and sad. Questions of "why me", and "why has this happened to me?" would only serve to torment me further and not offer any answers.

So I focused what energy I had on planning our wedding. I made the invitations, the table layout cards, and the table decorations. I organised the wedding favours, the photographer, and all the little incidentals as they arose. Everything took a long time, mainly because I needed to take regular breaks for rest and sleep. I organised my hen day at Bath Spa which consisted of relaxing treatments and some time in a lovely heated pool with five non running friends. The following day I completely crashed, I had no energy left to do anything but rest and sleep.

Paul and I were married at Malmesbury House and Gardens on the 13th September 2014 and it was a magical day. It was magical because, well, weddings generally are aren't they, especially for the bride and groom, but it was also magical because I somehow made it through the whole day and evening, with all the 'nice' stress of the ceremony, all the attention, the conversation, the busy atmosphere, and the dancing to the music in the evening. ME had granted me one day off, or maybe it was just the adrenalin taking over, for which I would pay in the coming days.

It did turn out to be the latter but we honeymooned in Spain, touring the beautiful countryside and stopping at little villages in our VW Campervan called Bali. I had plenty of time to rest and recover from that one perfect day.

We returned home and to the new normal. Paul working with clients in the studio and me doing very little. When I had the energy and some clarity in my brain I would research as much as I could about ME, things that might help me nutritionally, or in any other way. I went down so many rabbit holes looking for answers, clinging to stories of hope and quite possibly driving myself crazy, but I felt that I just needed to do something, I couldn't allow my life to be taken without a fight. There was so much more that I wanted to do with my life although I could only see that on days when I achieved some kind of positivity or hope. There were many more days which contained nothing hopeful, just loss and sadness and despair.

On the 15th of October I finally had a long awaited appointment with the much renowned Professor Vinod Patel at the George Eliot Hospital in Warwickshire. He was the only doctor at the time who had a specialist in Chronic Fatigue and ME so I was quite excited to have an appointment with him and suddenly very hopeful of finding answers to get me out of the grips of the horrible illness. It took about three hours to drive to the hospital for my appointment and I couldn't help thinking that this was going to be the start of my recovery which would eventually lead to me regaining my fitness and returning to my life. Sitting in the waiting room I watched as other people with ME went in for their appointments, then came out after about 15 minutes and left. Others arrived after me and sat on the empty chairs vacated by the previous patients. But I could not sense any hope in the room, just a kind of acceptance of limitations, of an illness within them that had left their life lifeless. Finally my name was called but I was already beginning to wonder if I'd set my expectations too high. During the all too brief time that I was sat in front of Professor Vinod Patel I slowly began to realise that there was no miracle, that everything I'd read about ME being a complicated and as yet incurable illness was in fact true, and I was now at the beginning of a very different and slower way of life. All Professor Patel could do was prescribe a care plan which included medication to help with the symptoms that I was suffering. So I took the prescriptions and left, feeling much like I'd imagined the previous patients were feeling when I saw them leave. I have to say at this point that my experience is in no way reflective of the care that Professor Vinod Patel provided. He genuinely came across as a very caring professional and listened intently to everything I told him about how the illness affected me. But one of the problems with ME is that it affects different people in different ways, which makes it almost impossible to find the exact cause and therefore to treat and cure the illness.

The medication that I was prescribed was mainly to treat the muscle and joint pain. By this time I had also been suffering with a constant headache for about six months. I woke up with this headache, it stayed with me all day long and I went to sleep with it still there. If I woke in the night the headache was the first thing I felt and that was the way it had been for around six months, no day off, no respite, and it didn't feel like it was going anytime soon.

I am reminded of how I felt during these times from my posts on Facebook and on 27th October I wrote "*I've just had one of those nights where I didn't want to go to sleep because I felt so ill that I was afraid that I wouldn't wake up again*". I frequently had those fears when I went to bed but there were also times when I was in so much pain and felt so bad that as I went to sleep I sometimes hoped that I wouldn't wake up again because I didn't want to have to face another day feeling that way.

Author Paul Tomkins writes of his experience of ME in an article entitled 'We Are Death, Warmed Up' and is worth reading if you want to understand more. Here is a short sample

We Are Death, Warmed Up
By Paul Tomkins

It is torture, of a kind. The unrelenting jab of needles into the spine.

The vice clamped to the temples and tightened.

The syringes slowly draining blood from the thighs, injecting concrete into the calves.

Poison swelling in the stomach, pumping to the veins, tying knots in the guts.

You shake, but not in terror. Even the twilight is too bright.

Movement sets flotsam and jetsam tumbling about the head; simply sitting up can be a struggle – postural hypertension sending you giddy.

Sights and sounds take longer to travel to the brain, the neural pathways fogged and furred with white noise and static.

You are death, ever so slightly warmed up.

During a totally unrelated sequence of events I by chance discovered that my father had died two years previously. I hadn't had any contact from him since 1996 when he and my step mother left me in no doubt that they didn't want me or my children in their lives. I can remember being sat at the bottom of the stairs listening to my younger half-brother tell me when and how he had died. It came as a shock, and I was angry that no one had tried to contact me over the past two years to tell me of his passing, and if it were not for my search for answers to questions I had surrounding my deceased grandparents I may never have found out about my father's demise. More facts came to light over the following few months, one of them was that during his funeral it was stated that he'd had three children, my half-brother and half-sister by my father's first marriage and my half-brother by his third marriage. I was his daughter by his second marriage and was not mentioned at all, it was as if I never existed. I didn't think I could be hurt any more by my family, I was wrong.

2014 had been quite a year, changing my life in so many ways. Yes, it wasn't all bad, there had been some big high points with getting engaged and then married, and enjoying the wonderful honeymoon with my new husband. But there were also some very deep lows with the diagnosis of an incurable illness, family heartbreak with my daughter, finding out my father had died years before, and feeling so ill that I was losing the motivation to go on. My once fit, strong, ultra running body was now struggling to just climb a few stairs and I needed to find a way back, somehow.

CHAPTER 7

MYALGIA ENCEPHALOMYELITIS

You can't help but learn a lot about an illness when it has invaded your body. My parents used to call me stubborn but that stubbornness was a strength that actually saved me many times, and it would again.

Ironically it wasn't until I had ME that I discovered there is an ME Awareness Day. In fact there had been an International ME Awareness Day on May 12th every year since 1992 and I had no real awareness of what the illness actually was or how it affected so many lives, and neither did most of the people I spoke to about my diagnosis. I discovered that it was an illness which was very misunderstood to varying degrees from believing that it doesn't actually exist, or it's all in the mind, to thinking it was just about feeling tired all the time. It's easy to forgive anyone who thought that because before I became sick that is what I thought too.

American born Thomas Michael Hennessy, Jr created

International ME Awareness Day and chose May 12th because it was the birthdate of Florence Nightingale who, it is suggested in some medical journals, also suffered from an illness very similar to ME.

Tom Hennessy suffered with ME from 1987 until his death, aged just 59, in 2013. Throughout his illness, even though for much of it he was bedridden and/or in chronic pain, Tom campaigned for more research and more effort into understanding ME, especially when the illness was grouped with many many others and put under the Chronic Fatigue Syndrome umbrella. In 1989 Tom made a speech at the very first International CFS Meeting in which he said the following

> "*We are NOT sick of being tired, we are tired of being SICK!" There is a HUGE difference!! Webster's Dictionary says "to define is to make clear and distinct, to differentiate". If you do NOTHING else today, lock the doors and come up with an accurate definition and change the God Damn Name! If you do not have the courage to do this today, you will condemn untold millions of people from all over the world to lives of abject misery, premature deaths and a huge economic burden on our societies. Knock heads until you come up with an accurate definition and a proper name*"

Tom's full testimony is available online and linked to his page on MEpedia which I will note at the back of this book should you choose to read more about this remarkable man. Suffice to say, he didn't mince his words. You could say that

Tom was an activist born out of inactivity due to the illness. What energy he did have, when he was physically able to, he would put it into fighting for the rights of others like himself.

But even after so many years of campaigning from what I can see, very little has changed. There are numerous support groups and associations and the awareness is expanding, but for the sufferers themselves it still seems to be the same story that I heard in 2014 in that there is no cure. This is possibly because the medical scientists still don't understand why the illness suddenly attacks someone out of the blue, or how it takes over the body and incapacitates that person to such a degree that they're unable to move, they feel constant chronic pain in joints and muscles, cannot think in any logical way whatsoever, cannot speak, word-find or hold any kind of conversation, amongst many other symptoms. It must be quite a conundrum and, as the same for many illnesses and conditions, there's not enough funding for the research.

In May 2016 an activist in America started the #MillionsMissing protest which became a global annual event. The protests now take place in September and October around the world and demonstrate for ME health equality in research funding, medical training and clinical trials. With long covid now in the mix, which has very similar symptoms to ME, and taking many more people out of society and into the welfare system, maybe there will be more funding allocated to finding answers to the questions this illness creates and more importantly an end to the long term suffering.

I had to go to a private hospital to get a diagnosis because my experience of trying to get help from my GP was fairly typical at the time. Even after my diagnosis my GP was reluctant to treat me and it became clear that he was of the opinion that ME didn't exist as a physical illness and as I was to discover many other doctors thought the same. I do hope that those opinions are now changed because they only add to the burden of the sufferer. I was eventually referred to a psychotherapist who recommended CBT (Cognitive Behavioural Therapy) and GET (Graded Exercise Therapy) and if I did not take up the appointments for those therapies then I would be deemed to 'not want help' and would be signed off. CBT not only suggests that the illness is all in the mind but would also be incredibly frustrating for someone who has severe brain fog, cannot think straight or discuss anything in detail, and GET can actually make the condition worse so I did not continue down that road. In communicating with other people with ME online I discovered that this was quite common practice, and as long as the clinician has seen you then you will become a statistic and nothing more.

Thomas Hennessy had fought for 25 years and ultimately lost the battle just as my fight was beginning. Somewhere deep down I still believed that I could find my way out of the ME maze, that the answer was out there somewhere, I just had to figure it out.

This photo encapsulates how I felt during my childhood
Even the fire had no comforting warmth

Little me in a troubled world

With the legend Ron Hill in Boston, US

Love and Strength, what I strive to live by

Comrades
2010

Craig Bridges pacing myself and others to a sub 6 minute mile.
I ran 5.49 that day, gasping for air!

Focused and ready for 105 laps of a track at the Andover Track marathon 2011 where I finished in 3:23:01 and 1st Female, six minutes ahead of 2nd place Female

Some of the special people who I call my family

This is me at my happiest

With Jen Coleman, receiving a prize from placing in the Ur City Ultra

Overjoyed to have won the ULTRArace Ladies Championship for the second time

At the start of the Thames Path 100 mile race in 2012

CHAPTER 8

THE WILDERNESS YEARS

January 2015 was typically cold and very wet but instead of enjoying the fact that I didn't have to go outside, not that I could anyway, the worse the weather got the more I wanted to go out in it, to battle against the winds, feel the cold rain on my skin and see my breath as ran up and down the hills around where we lived, to feel alive again.

I have always had a strong interest in complementary therapies and almost 20 years previously I qualified in a number of holistic therapies including reflexology, massage and aromatherapy. So when someone mentioned trying acupuncture, despite a normal aversion to needles, I immediately began researching local acupuncturists. I found a wonderful practitioner called Gisela Norman and from my first appointment I instinctively felt that this was going to be the start of my recovery. Thereafter I began weekly acupuncture sessions with Gisela. Every session would start with a consultation lasting about 10 to 15 minutes during which I would talk about how I was feeling mentally, emotionally and physically because although ME is a physical illness, all illnesses affect us in many more ways than just the physical. I can't say that I enjoyed the experience of having the needles placed but generally some were just a little uncomfortable and others I didn't feel at all. Very occasionally though there was one that really made me want to jump off the couch, thankfully that wasn't too often. Once all the needles were in place all I had to do was lie there on the couch and often I would drift into a light sleep. I saw Gisela almost every week for eight months and the acupuncture helped me enormously, relieving me of many symptoms and reducing others. However, if I had to miss a week for whatever reason I found that the symptoms would return very gradually so clearly there was still something else that I needed to do.

One of the research rabbit holes I found myself in talked about a link between mercury from dental fillings and ME. It was suggested that the toxic mercury leakage from old dental fillings could contribute to or even cause ME symptoms. This put me in another quandary because as a child of the 60's I had a lot of fillings. Back in those days most dentists drilled and filled teeth whether it was needed or not. I suspect it was a way of making money from the government under false pretences but with the confidence that no one would ever find out that they were drilling into perfectly healthy teeth. The dentist that my mother took me to every six months was brutal. It was never a simple check-up, the whole appointment was always a torturous experience where I would be held down on either side by the nurse and my mother whilst the dentist drilled into my teeth. It was as barbaric as it sounds. There were never any numbing injections back in those days either, not where I was taken to anyway. I would scream and cry and choke, and consequently I developed a strong phobia of dentists. So contemplating having all of my old fillings removed and replaced with a safer material put me in a real dilemma. Because of the health risks from the mercury as the fillings are removed they have to put a rubber dam into your mouth to stop pieces of the filling or vapour going down the throat, so you can only breathe through your nose, and for those reasons the procedure cannot be done under sedation. I desperately wanted to be well and believed that having my fillings removed and replaced could be at least a step closer to that, but on the other hand my phobia wouldn't even allow me to enter the main door of a dentist practice, much less get anywhere near a dentist chair. Paul found a dentist who was willing to do the work, but I said I'd think about it. Suffice to say it never happened.

In April I had another follow up appointment with Professor Vinod Patel. By now I had been prescribed various different medications. Some of which had made me feel very sick and some hadn't done anything at all but none of them had really helped me to feel in any way normal or decreased the pain significantly. I sat in the chair opposite Professor Patel in his consultation room and said that I was thinking of going along a more holistic route and asked for his opinion. He told me that if that was what my instinct was telling me to do then to go with it because the prescription medications are actually just toxins to the body trying to solve individual problems, and if you can find a more natural way to treat the whole body to feel better from the symptoms of ME then that would be the best outcome. He then said he would discharge me from his care, which frightened me a bit because it had been so difficult to get an appointment with him in the first place, but he added that if at any point I wanted to see him again I could just get a referral from my GP.

I felt like I was at the bottom of a mountain and there was no way round to the other side except up and over. Some days it just felt too hard and I couldn't see any kind of route through the wilderness. On one such day I wrote the following "And so it begins, today I threw away all my running socks, [which in all honesty was probably a good thing by that time], and all of my running shoes, aside from a couple of pairs I want to keep for sentimental reasons #feelingempty".

Two years previously, before we had any idea of what lay ahead, Paul and I had talked about moving to Spain and we had come up with a five year plan ending with relocating to southern Spain in 2018. We hadn't really spoken about it since, but I read that a warm climate can help relieve ME symptoms so one evening I brought up the subject of relocating to Spain and after a short discussion we decided to bring our plan to fruition. I tend to believe that when you are on the right path there are very few hurdles and that was the case with our move to Spain. We contacted estate agents in Spain and looked at properties online, creating a shortlist of properties to view in person. I strongly believed that I would get well soon after we settled in Spain and we would be able to start a new Personal Training business there. We decided that it would be more along the lines of an all-inclusive boot camp, where we would have six to eight places for athletes such as runners, cyclists, or triathletes on a week-long training camp. Along with specific training for the group, we would provide healthy nutritious meals on a full board basis. We would have a training area at the property and also take the group training on the beach. We even created a business plan and worked on the basis of having a planning week before the guests arrive, a week training, and then two weeks off before starting the process again. On the second of our two trips out to Spain to view potential properties we found a great property in Comares, Andalusia with enough accommodation and space inside and out to cater for the business. Everything was falling into place with ease and we were going to be living in Spain before the end of the year.

With the exciting prospect of our new life in Spain I was still trawling the internet looking for answers but now with a little more urgency and I came across CFS Health founded by someone in Melbourne, Australia who had suffered and recovered from ME himself. The website looked great and made big claims of how his program "provides hope, community and a step by step holistic program that helps brilliant people recover their health and life back". It sounded perfect and was exactly what I had been searching for so I signed up and paid the first instalment.

Although my time with CFS Health didn't end well, I did learn about my illness through the program, why my body was behaving as it was, and what I needed to do as a baseline to start my recovery so I did get something valuable for my money.

This is what I learned. It's already been established that ME tends to follow a virus of some kind, for me it was glandular fever, but if there are further stresses put on the body, physically and/or emotionally the autoimmune system, nervous system, digestive system and possibly other systems of the body become very sensitive and start a chain of reactions which causes the various symptoms of ME. It could be described like the workings of an electrical power breaker. If you plug a couple of things into a power breaker it can cope but as soon as you overload it or if something happens to one of the electrical devices then the power breaker shuts down the current.

So in order to get the body functioning normally again it was explained that you need to calm everything down and deal with each element that caused the body to break. The very first thing to do was establish a strict routine which meant everything had to have a time slot. The systems of the body prefer routine and it's suggested that it calms the adrenal system. So I put this into place and I would get up at exactly the same time, have the same morning routine, have breakfast at the same time every day, have a short morning activity at the same time, lunch at the same time, rest and have the same afternoon routine, have my evening meal at the same time of 7pm every day and always in bed by 10pm. This routine had to be kept exactly the same every day for a minimum of six weeks for the body to start to feel 'safe' again, removing all stress factors. That was the baseline. On top of that was attention to nutrition and hydration. I've been a vegetarian since I was about 18 or 19 and my diet had been pretty healthy for at least a good twenty years but it had to get healthier. We switched to organic as much as we could. Even though I only used to have one coffee a day I changed that to decaffeinated. I also cut my alcohol intake to just one drink at the weekend, cut down on sugar and I was drinking two to three litres of water a day.

The online recovery program also included worksheets to complete to help evaluate various aspects from activity to mental and emotional stability. To help the feeling of not being alone in the recovery journey there was also a private Facebook group where you could share experiences and seek advice. I was still within my first three months of the program and to an extent was still finding my feet. I was still battling with depression and hit a particularly low point so one evening I reached out to the people on the private Facebook group. The next morning I discovered that I had been locked out of the Facebook group without warning or reason. When I questioned why I was told in no uncertain terms that I had been 'too negative' in my reaching out for help. Of course I could ask for a one to one video call with one of Toby's team, obviously at an additional cost, but aside from that I was on my own. Needless to say, I didn't renew my subscription.

I did continue practising my strict daily routine though and was finding that very gradually I could do a little more without fear of crashing. The daily and even weekly differences were hardly noticeable but over a period of time I could look back and see that I was a little further away from the bottom of the mountain.

During one of my last acupuncture sessions with Gisela she brought up the subject of nutrition, and although with my vegetarian diet I had still been very watchful that I got all the right vitamins and minerals to help my body heal, Gisela asked me if I could consider eating chicken because it contained certain properties that she thought would help me. Having been a vegetarian for well over thirty years I struggled with just the thought of eating another once living creature, but at the time I was desperate to have my health back. I told Gisela that I would give it some thought. As I was paying for my session Gisela came out of her consultation room and said that there was another food with almost the same properties as chicken and that product is shiitake mushrooms. I breathed a sigh of relief knowing that I wouldn't have that extremely difficult decision to make, shiitake mushrooms became a regular staple in my diet, and still is.

On the internet there are so many suggested 'miracle cures' for numerous illnesses ranging from the seemingly ridiculous to possibly maybe. In my never ending search I stumbled across an article on geopathic stress and ley lines, and while there are many sceptics who do not believe in the phenomenon, there is some evidence that geopathic stress can have an effect on your overall health so I looked into it further.

When the earth's magnetic field is disturbed or disrupted by underground water streams, geological faults or fractures, mine or quarry works etc. it's claimed that this can cause geopathic stress lines of negative energies emanating from the earth. I asked my acupuncturist, Gisela, about her thoughts on the subject and she was wholeheartedly behind the subject and even knew a practitioner who tested homes for GS and offered solutions to any issues that were found. This got me thinking about the area in which I lived at the time. It's a very small but lovely country village, the type of village where you know almost everyone. But as I thought more it struck me how much illness there was among the people who lived there so I went ahead and had our home tested. The tests showed that there were geopathic stress lines going right up through our kitchen and bedroom above. We had a lovely big spacious bedroom with wonderful views of the countryside and a large ensuite and dressing room but I could no longer sleep there knowing that it could be affecting my health so we moved into a much smaller spare room on the other side of the house. I was so desperate that if someone told me that walking on hot coals blindfolded would help me to get well I would have done that without question.

On the 25th September 2015, with a heavy heart I closed my business. Top2Toe Fitness had ceased trading and my lovely clients would be searching out new personal trainers and massage therapists. Even now as I'm writing this book I look at the three years that I was running the business as the best time of my working career, it was truly a vocation that I loved.

On the 6th October I received a phone call telling me that my mother had died the previous day. I'd not had any contact from her since early 2008 and her last words to me were "Go to hell", something she had said to me before but the hell I'd previously gone to was trying to have a relationship with her. This time she said those words she made it clear that she couldn't be who I needed her to be. However I still wanted to attend her funeral, mainly for closure. My father's funeral had passed without me even knowing that he'd died so I felt that I needed to attend the funeral of one of my parents for my own sense of finality. Despite my cousin's promise that he'd give me the details of the funeral as soon as he knew when and where it was to be, I discovered a few weeks later that the funeral had happened and my aunts, uncles and cousins all attended but chose not to tell me.

This book should be about surviving my family, not recovering from ME! But those two things aren't necessarily mutually exclusive and I consider myself stronger and more determined because of how I've been treated, and mistreated by my family which meant that I wasn't going to give up on myself or on regaining my health.

We moved to Spain towards the end of 2015 and as with any house move, it was impossible to keep to the set routine that I had in the UK, but by now the results of my self-discipline were beginning to show and I had more energy and slightly less pain plus the headache had finally gone after thirteen continuous months of torture. I began to feel like I was making good progress towards getting my health back and I tentatively started to entertain the idea of trying a little run. By the middle of January I had talked myself into it and on the 22nd January 2016 with my stomach doing somersaults I put on my running kit and went out for a few easy miles. I started about 3 miles from our home in Spain and it was all downhill to our casa. It was a beautiful warm sunny day, the scenery was simply stunning and running down the side of the road I was the happiest I'd been in a long time. Clearly I had made some progress, but I was definitely not out of the woods by any means because the following day my energy crashed and it would be a number of days before I felt well again. I didn't regret the run though, it told me that I was going in the right direction but that it was just going to take more time and patience.

The only problem was that with every gain came a fall. Paul took me to Granada in Spain for my birthday in March, which obviously involved some sightseeing, and walking around the beautiful city. I was beginning to enjoy life a bit more and pushed boundaries a little. Consequently a few days after my birthday I crashed and was confined to the couch once again. I knew I couldn't keep doing that if I was to stay on the path to recovery. It was a very fine balancing act between activity and rest.

2016 rolled on relentlessly and there were some big distractions that year (don't mention the B word!) but I was still having periods of time where I was haunted by not being able to run. It wasn't just the physical part of running that I missed, I felt like I didn't belong anywhere, a big important part of my personal identity was missing and I felt lost. So I came to a decision that I needed to move on and find something else to do with my life. To explore that I started a blog on blogspot.com (now blogger.com). Writing my thoughts created space in my mind for possibilities, it cleared the weeds to make room for the tiny shoots that would eventually grow into something even stronger. During my visit to South Africa in 2011 when I ran Comrades for the second time I went on a safari in Kruger National Park and one of the photos I took is of two elephants with their trunks intertwined. That photo is my Facebook cover photo and I love the symbolism of strength and power that it exudes. Depression has cloaked me many times before and since but that image somehow manages to inspire a strength in me, to stay entwined in life and not let go.

We had settled into the more relaxed Spanish way of life quite easily, although naturally I put pressure on myself to get well so we could make plans to start the new business. I realised that this pressure wasn't helping me so with some regret and to remove any unnecessary pressure we decided to let go of the business idea for the time being. With that off my mind I was once again one hundred percent focused on what I could do for myself. I explored some other complementary therapies, one of which was 'Reconnective Healing'. I had studied complementary health therapies myself during 1999 – 2004 and I am qualified in Reflexology, Aromatherapy, Crystal Energy Healing, and a range of massage therapies including Sports Massage, Hot Stone Massage and Indian Head Massage so I am generally open minded to healing therapies, but I'm not sure that reconnective healing did anything other than completely relax me for the hour that I was laid on the couch, I certainly didn't 'feel' anything and I can't say with any conviction that it helped any of the symptoms of ME that I was experiencing at the time. However, attending the healing centre every two weeks connected me with various people and introduced me to another therapist and type of healing that would eventually be the missing piece of the jigsaw that I was looking for.

At the end of December 2017 I watched a documentary that flicked a switch in me and subtly changed my thinking. The documentary is called 'Heal' and I remember watching it totally transfixed and hanging on to every word. It talks about the body's ability to heal itself in a way that makes absolute sense. One of the messages that came through was that you just have to get 'yourself' out of the way. A quote from the documentary really struck me and I carried it forward from that point on. The quote was "Believe the diagnosis, don't believe the prognosis".

PART **THREE**

CHAPTER 9

THE YEAR EVERYTHING CHANGED

Often it's the deepest pain
which empowers you to grow
into your highest self
Karen Salmansohn

The year 2018 arrived and it was now over four years since I became ill. Four years isn't long in terms of having ME, many people suffer the worst symptoms for ten, twenty or more years and even then never really break free completely but manage their lives around the illness, having ME dictate what they can and can't do on an almost daily basis for the remainder of their lives. I have never liked being told what I can and can't do (within reason) so I was never prepared to accept that I was going to be controlled by ME for the rest of my life. Yes, I had the illness but I never accepted it as a part of who I was. It was happening to me rather than living in me.

Someone told me about Theta Healing and suggested that it may help me and after reading a little about it I was intrigued and willing to give it a go. At the healing centre where I went for reconnective healing I heard about a lady who practised Theta Healing from her home less than an hour's drive away so I contacted her to make the appointment. But when I heard how much she charged per session I was reluctant, especially not knowing how many sessions I would need or indeed if it would definitely help me. She then said that no one should be denied healing due to cost and offered to provide the session at a reduced price so I booked my first session for the 9th March.

The Theta Healing Practitioner, a lady who goes by the name of Anne Zipse, welcomed me in and I sat in a chair opposite her, really not knowing what to expect. Anne asked me what I needed help with so I explained about the illness and that I'd been trying to get well for a number of years. She then asked me about my history and I briefly told her about my childhood, family and experiences growing up. From what I have learnt since my first session with Anne is that not all experiences of Theta healing are the same, just like many treatments it very much depends on the individual so I'm not going to write about everything that happened in that first session because it's my experience and may not necessarily be the same as the way other people might experience Theta Healing but I will give you my understanding of how it worked for me in that first session. Anne's questions delved deep into my past causing me to think about my feelings as I was growing up. Old emotions rose to the surface with the insecurities and beliefs I held as a child. After exploring this for a period of time Anne then used a technique known as 'muscle testing'. There are various ways of using this technique but for me it involved holding my forefinger and thumb together forming an O. After testing 'yes' in which my thumb and finger would stay strong and touching when Anne tried to part them, and 'no' in which my thumb and forefinger could easily be parted, Anne then gave me a phrase to repeat. The phrase could be anything from "I am loved" to "I deserve to be happy" or "I'm good enough" and many others, depending on what the situation is that is being worked on. Some of the results really surprised me, in as much as I was totally unaware of some of my deeply held beliefs about myself. Muscle testing reveals your true deeply held beliefs at a subconscious level which can be created from a very young age, so even though I held certain conscious beliefs as an adult, my subconscious apparently had a whole other agenda and it's generally the subconscious beliefs that have the ultimate power in how you might react to something. Having discovered what my 'mistaken beliefs' were, Anne then took me into a meditative state. I was totally awake and aware but with my eyes closed, and she guided me through a vision in my mind. Anne then asked for the mistaken beliefs to be deleted and replaced by the positive opposite. This only lasted a few minutes and my beliefs were again checked using the muscle testing technique. The altered results were astonishing! We went through this sequence a number of times and at the end of the hour I felt like I had been relieved of a huge weight of emotional baggage that had been created by my family over my formative years. Since my first bout of depression at the age of 18 and throughout further periods of depression and suicidal thoughts and actions in the following years I'd had too many hours to count of talking therapy with some amazing and caring psychotherapists, but what I had achieved with Anne in that hour was way beyond anything I'd experienced in counselling. As I got up to leave Anne said that if I wanted to make another appointment she was confident that she could help me with the ME. Anne advised me to leave it about four weeks to let the work we'd done that day settle but I felt so good that I was keen to make another appointment. I called Anne after a couple of weeks to book in and she had had a cancellation for the 29th March so I booked in without hesitation.

I sat in the chair opposite Anne and now knowing what to expect I was prepared to get to work. I felt confident that Anne would be able to help me but I wasn't prepared for what was about to happen at the end of the hour. We talked about the illness, how it affected me and how it impacted on my life. Anne asked me about my thoughts and feelings with my illness, how it had changed my life and lifestyle and how that made me feel. I told her that I hated being ill, that I wanted to be healthy and would do anything to have my life back. We then went through some muscle testing. Anne asked me to hold my thumb and forefinger together and repeat after her "I deserve to be ill". I did as she asked and as I said "I deserve to be ill" Anne tried to part my finger and thumb, but to my surprise they stayed strong. Anne gave me another phrase to repeat "My body knows how to heal itself" and this time my finger and thumb parted easily. I remember being totally shocked, thinking how could this be? I believed in healing and had studied therapies on assisting the body to heal, and used them on myself, plus I had spent over four years trying to get my health back, but at the same time I believed that not only did my body not know how to heal itself but also held the belief that I actually deserved to be ill! This was a complete revelation to me and on reflection I can understand how those beliefs might have been created.

As a young child I suffered regularly with excruciatingly painful bouts of what they used to call a 'grumbling appendix'. My mother wasn't the 'mothering' type so dealing with me when I was sick and/or in pain was left to my father. But his bedside manner also left a lot to be desired and when I think back to those times when I was in a lot of pain all I remember is my father being angry and shouting questions at me asking if he should call a doctor or not. I must have been between the ages of seven to nine years old and I was made to feel like I was an inconvenience when I was sick and in pain. I eventually had my appendix removed at the age of ten and that's another horrific memory altogether. My parents left me at the hospital, didn't visit and I was alone and frightened. For some reason I was not on a children's ward either and I remember seeing the adult in the bed opposite me. She looked as if she felt sorry for me as I was taken to the operating theatre. The nightmare became like a horror movie in the operating theatre. I can still remember quite clearly seeing the big light above me and being surrounded by people in masks. Someone was trying to get a needle in my hand but I was crying and struggling so much out of pure fear that the needle didn't stay in and blood pooled under the skin of my hand causing it to rise up in a lump. When I saw that I screamed and panicked even more. They must have managed to sedate me soon after because I don't remember anything from that point until after the operation. I was so very thirsty but I wasn't allowed to have any water. There was no cup, but a jug of water had been left on the table and I remember that I was so desperate for water that I picked it up and began gulping straight from the jug. Thankfully hospitals are much more child friendly these days.

While I was still reeling from the revelations of my deeply held beliefs Anne continued to work without missing a beat. She took me into the meditative state as before and deleted the beliefs that were keeping me sick, replacing them with a more realistic and positive set of beliefs. Anne then used the muscle testing technique on me one last time and asked me to repeat the same phrases as before. This time as I said "I deserve to be ill" my forefinger and thumb parted with ease and when I repeated "My body knows how to heal itself" my thumb and finger stuck together like glue. The work was done and my hour was up. What happened next took my breath away. I stood up out of the chair and I felt a huge wave of energy flood through my body, something I'd never felt before or since. I asked Anne if I needed to make another appointment and she said no, it's not necessary, and that I should just go out and get back into the life I wanted. When it came to pay for the hour Anne charged me the lower rate as she had on my previous appointment but I said no, and gave her the original higher fee, it was nothing compared to what she had given me.

On March 29th 2018 Anne Zipse gave me my life back, I was healthy and totally free from ME at last. My body was functioning normally again.

I know all this might sound fantastical and when I arrived home that afternoon and told Paul what had happened and that I didn't have ME anymore he initially didn't believe it but I knew how different I felt and knew that he would eventually see the difference too. It felt like my body had suddenly woken up from a long deep sleep.

How I see it now is that in everything I did, all the changes and adjustments to diet and lifestyle that I made through the years that I was ill before the theta treatments, put my body into the best position it could be in and the final piece in the puzzle was in my subconscious beliefs which were accessed and changed through Theta Healing allowing my body to physically heal itself.

Two days later I travelled to the UK to see my daughter on her 28th birthday. I had so much energy that I didn't know what to do with it, I couldn't sit still and was literally bouncing off the walls. I felt more alive than I could remember feeling and just wanted to shout from the rooftops how wonderful I felt.

As much as I sometimes wish I'd never signed up to Facebook for a myriad of reasons, it's occasionally good to look back at times like these and on the 19th April I posted this:

Having a moment…

Just thinking about the fact that I am now restored to complete health, after over 4 years of being ill.

I'm now living in Spain HEALTHY for the first time!

I have more energy than I know what to do with (although I've got plenty of ideas).

I have everything I need, and more.
I have amazing friends in my life.

I felt so grateful and couldn't have been happier. Paul was also moved to shout about it too and posted this:

> *Today my incredible wife Trinity Buckley has been free of ME for 3 weeks.*
>
> *After 4 whole years of having her life and energy drained from her, and the woman I met transformed from a ball of energy, living life on the edge, who could tackle anything, to at times, an empty shell, not able to function, contribute or look forwards.*
>
> *She was a total inspiration before ME, living life to the full, and during ME also, because despite many ups and downs she always carried on looking for an answer, never giving up, always bouncing back.*
>
> *She found it in Theta Healing.*
>
> *Now again we have endless opportunities to explore, Trinity can take on whatever challenges she wants and I feel like the luckiest man in the world to have back the force of nature I first met, brimming with life and energy.*
>
> *I wanted to post this brief tale to encourage other ME sufferers to keep looking, keep trying things and find your answer to the puzzle. Don't settle.*

By the end of April I had started strength training and I also had a shiny new Garmin watch on my wrist. I had lost all of my running fitness and much of my strength so I was starting from scratch, but it was a challenge I was totally up for. On the 1st of May I started the Couch to 5k which is a running schedule designed for absolute beginners. The first session was run for 1 minute then walk for 1 minute and repeat that 10 times. I'm not ashamed to say that I struggled, but I also enjoyed every single second. It was evident that I had a very long way to go to get back to the fitness I had enjoyed pre ME (if indeed I could) but I had started on that journey and I was going to enjoy the ride.

As my body got used to this new exercise regime there were a few hiccups, my back became quite sore and I had to have a short break from the schedule to let it heal but I remained active and I had a sudden desire to climb a mountain! Living in Andalusia we have a wonderful view of Mount Maroma. La Maroma, also known as Tejeda, is the highest peak of the Sierra de Tejeda, Spain at an altitude of 2069m. The summit is located in the region of Axarquía on the border between the provinces of Granada and Málaga. Paul had wanted to climb it since we moved to Spain but had not yet had the opportunity. But he was away with a mate on a motorbike trip to Portugal for a few days and I had bundles of energy and itchy feet. So I contacted a couple of friends to ask if they would like to join me and the day was set for 13th May, which coincidentally was the day after International ME Awareness Day.

There were five of us that day, two friends with their partners and me. It was a beautiful day, although a little cool when we started at 8am. I was wearing a back support to help my back while it was still healing and the first hour or so was a reasonably easy walk up a concrete track which zigzagged up the base of the mountain. From leaving the track to the summit it was about 4 hours of hiking over rocky trails, through forested areas and finally ascending up over large boulders which opened out onto a flattish area with the most stunning 360 degree views. On a clear day, sun haze permitting, it's possible to see Africa from one side of the summit and Sierra Nevada in mainland Spain on the other.

Reaching the top of the mountain was a significant moment for me. It was like I had been climbing a mountain for the past four years and there were times that it felt so tough that I didn't think I would ever make it to the top. On the summit of Maroma there is an obelisk and without hesitation I climbed to the very top of it. I stood at the highest point on Maroma that day and realised that my fight was over. What I had achieved since the end of 2013 was above all else my greatest achievement in life so far. The descent was a little harder on my back but we were all down off the mountain in about 3 hours. It was a day that I will never forget.

Opportunities were presenting themselves continuously. A couple of years previously Paul and I had talked about travelling to Peru and visiting Machu Picchu. I knew that I wouldn't be able to walk the Inca Trail but I'd read that there was a train that could take you most of the way. The idea came back to me and we decided to start planning our trip for the following year, but we wouldn't be getting the train, hiking the Inca Trail on foot sounded like much more fun.

On the 13th July I'd progressed through the couch to 5k schedule and was able to run for twenty minutes without stopping. Two weeks later I managed four miles non-stop running in 35 minutes and 12 seconds. I was on a runner's high and on the spur of the moment I decided to set a goal, increase my training and enter the Malaga Marathon in December.

My first race since my recovery was a 5km Parkrun in Cirencester. I hadn't started a race in a very long time and I was more nervous than I could ever remember being at any start line, ever. My whole body was physically shaking with nerves and I felt like I was an absolute beginner to running. But in true Parkrun tradition, everyone was very friendly and I got chatting to a couple of people, one of whom has remained a good friend. It's interesting how the right people tend to come into your life at the right time. This lady used running as part of her therapy having sadly lost her sister quite suddenly. We talked about our anxieties and she told me about techniques which had helped her.

The Parkrun in Cirencester was three laps of a muddy course and once I got started I immediately began to feel more relaxed. I'd missed that feeling of racing with other people and it felt good to push my body a little harder than I had in my training. I finished strong in 26:57 and placed 1st LV55!

My marathon training was going well and on the 18th November in torrential rain I completed a training run of 20 miles in 3 hours and 7 minutes, six days later I returned to the Cirencester Parkrun, much less nervous and finished in 24:29, almost two and a half minutes faster than the previous attempt. The following day I was at another start line, this time it was a half marathon in Wiltshire. I enjoyed every minute of the race and when I crossed the finish line in a time of 1:49:07 I had the biggest smile on my face! I was also 5th LV50! The Malaga marathon was just two weeks away and I felt ready.

On the 9th of December I stood in my start pen of the marathon and felt a huge well of emotion rising through me. It had been quite a year and 2018 was ending in a way that I could never have dreamed of. Just eight and a half months after my full recovery from ME I ran the Malaga marathon with my heart and soul and crossed the finish line in four hours, six minutes and eight seconds.

In 2018 I ran 588.8 miles.

CHAPTER 10

THE YEAR BEFORE COVID

The year 2019 got off to a great start with a 1 hour 55 minute half marathon in Torremolinos in February, a 46:16 and 1st LV55 at the Torre Del Mar 10k in March, followed a week later by the Barcelona Marathon where I finished in 3 hours 54 minutes and 18 seconds. On the 29th March we celebrated the first anniversary of my return to health, and if anyone had said to me on that day just one year before that I would run a sub four hour marathon within a year I would never have believed them. Life can be full of surprises!

The trip to Peru followed and over the four weeks of May we went backpacking across Peru, hopping on and off buses and staying in hostels along the way. When we were planning the trip I happened to notice that there was a marathon in Lima and as luck (or fate) would have it, we would actually be in Lima over that very weekend. It would be rude not to join in so I booked my place in the marathon while Paul entered the 10 km race. It was a fantastic experience to run the marathon in Peru and I enjoyed every minute but the main event of our trip was trekking the full Inca Trail to Machu Picchu. A couple of days before we were due to start the trek I became suddenly and very violently sick with a gastric parasite which had entered my system via a cup of herbal tea! I was so sick that I was admitted to hospital in Cusco and on intravenous anti-parasitic drugs for about 36 hours. I was discharged from hospital one day before the trek and felt so weak but nothing was going to stop me from taking on this part of the trip. It was a wonderful experience and parts of the route were so stunningly beautiful that it actually brought me to real emotional tears. We had a guide who pointed out amazing flora and fauna, the tiniest orchids you could ever see and really beautiful humming birds that were so close to us that it felt like they were granting us the privilege of seeing them perform. He took us on a magical tour and told us about the history of the Inca trail, the monuments along the way, and of course all about Machu Picchu itself when we finally arrived at the site. The whole trip was an experience that I will never forget.

By the end of the year I had run a further three ten kilometre races, four half marathons, and three more marathons including a 3 hour 52 minute finish in Malaga, which was a full fourteen minutes faster than the previous year, and a 3 hour 47 minute finish in Valencia. I was back with a capital B.

It almost felt like the ME years were just a long nightmare, or was I just having the best dream now and about to wake up to that old reality. Friends who had witnessed my return to life contacted me to ask how I'd recovered and I recounted my story over and over. Sometimes a friend would ask if they could put someone who had ME in touch with me to see if I could help them and of course I always agreed. Some contacted me, some didn't but I tried to share my experience wherever I could in the hope that at least one person would find a way out as I did. I tried to inspire people who had the illness to not give up, to not accept that that was how their life was always going to be. I understand that ME affects different people in different ways, which is one of the reasons why it's so hard to diagnose, but if you can just find the root I believe it's possible to make the changes that you need to help the body to heal.

Occasionally I would feel frustrated when I tried to help another sufferer and they would make excuses or give reasons as to why the things I suggested wouldn't work for them. But I just had to accept that everyone is on their own life path, and some people can accept what has happened to them, come to terms with it and settle. That doesn't reflect anything back on me, it's just the way people are, all different with different agendas and life experiences.

In 2019 I ran 1424 miles, and 2012.8 miles since recovering from ME.

I'd entered another marathon in Spain which was in the diary for February 2020. It was the Castellon marathon and I was hoping for a sub 3.45 hour finish. On the drive up to the province of Valencia we kept hearing about this virus which was making a lot of people ill in China and some were even dying. Little did we know what was about to happen.

I didn't quite achieve my time goal in the marathon.

I ran most of it with the sub 3.45 pacer but I had some stomach issues towards the end which cost me some time in the toilets of a Spanish bar. I still got across the finish line in 3 hours and 48 minutes though and won first in my age group, which was a bonus.

I returned to the Torre Del Mar 10k race in March 2020. The virus that we'd heard about was travelling through Europe by now and I remember standing at the start line feeling quite uneasy about being so close to a lot of people. I was wearing a buff and pulled it up over my mouth and nose while we waited for the race to start. I had a great race, finishing nearly three minutes faster than the previous year in 43:31, and again on the centre of the podium for 1st LV55 holding my prize, which was a full tray of avocados!

One week later everyone was on lockdown.

CHAPTER 11

COVID TIMES

Spain went on a full lockdown officially on 16th March 2020 and it was one of the strictest lockdowns in Europe, we were not even allowed out for exercise, which was a tad inconvenient because I'd planned for 2020 to be the year that I returned to ultra running. But it was all about keeping ourselves and others safe so it was easy to comply. However, we do live up on the mountain trails so I did venture out a few times and each time I didn't see a soul. I did enter a couple of 50 mile ultras but they were not until September and of course everything would be back to normal by then, wouldn't it?

As time went on it became clear that the virus was not going away any time soon and seemed to be intent on destroying as many lives, families, plans, and businesses as possible. Training for races lost its importance and running purely to maintain some kind of sanity took precedence. We are fortunate to have a reasonable amount of space around our house and I created a lap of which twenty would be equal to one mile. The most laps I ran in one go was 120 making 6 mind numbing miles, but from what I saw on the news I was by far not the only one resorting to exercising in this way. Of course famously there was Captain Tom walking laps for charity at the grand age of 100, but there were also many more unsung heroes running laps of their house, their gardens, even their driveways for varying reasons from raising funds for desperate charities, to personal challenges or like me, to keep some semblance of sanity. Although running 120 laps of a terrace to maintain sanity could be considered an oxymoron. The most impressive 'home run' that I read about was of a man from South East London who ran a marathon in his own back garden. It was reported that he ran a continuous 873 laps of his garden in four hours and fifty seven minutes raising over £3000 for a cancer charity. That puts my 120 lap six miler into perspective!

September arrived and the world was still a very long way from being back to normal and many people, including myself, thought that we were going to be living in a new normal with the social distancing and mask wearing here to stay. I have to say that I am very happy that I was wrong.

Although many races were cancelled or postponed that year, both of the 50 mile ultras that I'd entered went ahead because with staggered starts it was possible to be completely distanced from fellow runners and other people along the route. There were also strict rules about testing before leaving home, regular sanitising and minimising touch points during the race. On the 12th September I was in the UK for the White Horse 50 mile ultra. I probably could have picked a tougher 50 mile race for my first ultra back, but not by much. The course was worth the work though and took us through some stunning Wiltshire countryside with 1340 metres of elevation providing views to take what's left of your breath away. The reason it's called the White Horse ultra is because the route passes five horses which are cut into the hills and turf of the chalk landscape. It also visits many other historic and prehistoric locations, passing close to the start of the Ridgeway National Trail. Towards the end I got horribly lost in the woods, ended up sliding down a steep bank and not being able to get back up. Hoping to get the attention of any other runner who may be passing I shouted for help, but to no avail. There was no choice but to try and get myself back up the bank and with tears rolling down my face I dug my fingers in the ground and got hold of tree roots and anything I could find to pull me up out of the ditch. I eventually made it, composed myself and tried to figure out which direction I needed to go to get to the finish, which was actually only about three miles away. My navigational skills had certainly not improved over the years that I was away from running. I finally crossed the finish line in 11 hours and 55 minutes, and third in my age group, out of three. More importantly, I could now call myself an ultra runner again.

One week later I ran the Leviathlon 50 mile race, organised by Phoenix Running. This was a much easier race than the previous week with just 114 metres of ascent over a 15 lap course alongside a river in Hertfordshire. It was not as scenic but also impossible to get lost so I enjoyed the event for different reasons and finished this one two hours quicker in 9 hours 54 minutes.

Undeterred by the pandemic and spurred on by these two races I came up with a plan to run three big ultras in 2021 for a charity close to my heart. The three ultras were the South Downs Way 100 in June, the Al Andalus Ultimate Trail in July and the North Downs Way 100 in August. I had eight months to prepare myself to run a hilly 100 miles and I was looking forward to the long weekend runs over the local mountain trails. On one particular trail run in October, only a few miles from home I saw a car coming towards me. I was as far into the bank at the side of the road as I could be without falling into the ditch. Suddenly the car picked up speed and drove directly at me. The car hit me and I went over the corner of his bonnet and landed in a ditch on my back. The driver didn't stop, he just continued driving but I was too shocked to get his registration so he was never caught. I lay there for a few minutes in tears and some lovely Spanish people stopped to help me. Thankfully, apart from the shock of the incident, I got away with just bruises and a sore back, but it could have been a lot worse. As I write this, two years on, I can still clearly visualise the front of the grey car coming towards me and remember the feeling of fear and panic. Hopefully the driver eventually received his share of karma.

In 2020 I ran 1925.8 miles, and 3938.6 miles since recovering from ME.

CHAPTER 12

ONE OUT OF THREE AIN'T GOOD

I worked hard on my training for what I called the 'Triple Challenge', steadily increasing the weekly mileage and completing back to back long runs on the weekends. I spent hours on rocky trails running fifty to fifty five mile weekends and by June I was in great shape and ready for the first event, the South Downs Way 100 which would take place on 12th and 13th of that month. We travelled to our little holiday home in the UK, all the planning had been done, all the kit was ready and I felt eager to get to the start line.

In the very early hours of Wednesday 9th June our dogs were barking downstairs, so I got up and went to quieten them down. In my sleepy state I slipped on the stairs. I didn't slip far though, it just startled me more than anything. Having quietened the dogs I returned to bed. As I got out of bed the next morning I could feel that the heel of my right foot was quite sore. I didn't pay too much attention to it though and carried on with the day. On Thursday morning it was still quite sore so I thought I'd go out for an easy few miles to see how it felt to run on. The verdict was not good so I rested for the remainder of the day, believing that there was time for it to settle down before the start line on Saturday. On Friday morning I got out of bed and I could not put any weight at all on my right foot. As I crawled to the bathroom on all fours I tried to push away the thoughts that were racing through my mind about how I was going to run 100 hilly miles that weekend. In my desperate state I even contacted the organiser asking if it would be possible to complete the course on crutches. They did not dignify my question with an answer.

Paul drove me to the Accident and Emergency department of the local hospital and as he carried me through the doors the receptionist came rushing out with a wheelchair thinking it was something very serious. After examination and x-rays it turned out that I had cracked my heel bone. I was fitted for a big boot, given crutches and was told that it would take around six to eight weeks to heal. I was devastated. Not only would I not be able to run the South Downs Way 100, my continued training for the second event, Al Andalus (AAUT) plus the race itself was also in question.

I didn't run at all for almost three weeks and as AAUT got closer I decided to go for a very gentle four miles. Feeling optimistic I went for another run two days later, extending to six miles. I ran twice more before AAUT with rest days in between and, feeling quietly confident, we drove to Loja for the start of the 5 stage race.

I'd never taken part in a stage race before so this was to

be a whole new experience. Added to that inland Spain in midsummer can get up to around 45 degrees centigrade and the race routes had very little if any shade. But I was simply happy to have made it to the start line.

The Al Andalus Ultimate Trail is a semi-supported five stage, 234 km (145.4 mile) ultra marathon race in Andalusia. Each day offers a new running challenge through the Poniente Granadino, ending in different villages to enjoy the culture and ambiance of the beautiful Granada Province. The challenges, aside from the distance, include the hot dry weather, and the diverse and at times technical terrain, but the rewards are plentiful through the scenic natural parks. Between the stages we camped in little tents and the high temperatures of the day plummeted overnight making getting under the freezing cold shower sometimes as challenging as the race itself.

The first stage was 38 km from Loja to Alhama de Granada, with a total ascent of 1170 metres and total descent of 920 metres. I completed stage one reasonably comfortably in a time of 5:45:30. At the finish line of this and every stage we were welcomed with a bowl of water in which to soak our hot, tired and sore feet, and offered plates of watermelon and bowls of crisps, all very much appreciated after a long day out in the blazing sun.

The second stage was 48 km from Alhama de Granada to Játar, with a total ascent of 1440 metres and a total descent of 1350 metres. I completed stage two in 8:18:44

The third stage was 39 km from Játar to Jayena, with a total ascent of 850 metres and total descent of 915 metres. I completed it in 5:11:58 and I was surprised and delighted to find that I was the third female to finish that stage! There were different stage prizes each day, which were usually products from the local area of that particular stage. On that day the prize was a jar of bee pollen which was a little ironic given that Paul and I are beekeepers. We don't actually take pollen from our bees though, I think it's quite sad that the bees work so hard to forage and collect pollen from far and wide all day long and then as they get back to the hive it's stripped from them by a pollen collector fixed on the hive by the beekeeper, meaning they enter the hive with nothing for the colony. I know pollen has many good properties but I could never bring myself to do that to the bees.

The forth, longest and most difficult stage was 67 km from Jayena to Alhama de Granada, with a total ascent of 1300 metres and total descent of 1350 metres which I completed in 11:24:58. By the time I got to the finish of this stage I was not in a good way. My injured heel had been complaining causing me to alter how I ran which resulted in an ankle injury and huge blisters covering the sole of my foot. As the team medic patched me up he asked if I was going to be able to run the last stage. But for me that was never in question, I'd made it that far and I was not about to give up with just one stage to go, no matter how sore or broken I felt.

Stage five was 42 km from Alhama de Granada back to Loja where we had started at the beginning of the week, with a total ascent of 970 metres and a total descent of 1290 metres. That last long easy jog downhill was very welcome and I got to the final finish line in 5:57:43. My overall time for the 234 km was 36 hours, 38 minutes and 53 seconds but it wasn't really about the times for me, it was ultimately about the finish. Finishing meant that I was another step further from ME and another step closer to me.

The last event in my triple challenge was the North Downs Way 100 mile race, organised by Centurion Running, the same company who organise the South Downs Way. The weather in the UK can never be guaranteed but who knew how bad it would be on that summer weekend in early August. I was one of two hundred and four people to put themselves at the start line of this race. It was a staggered start time with covid precautions still in place and I was no more than a mile into my race when the rain started. Over the years I have run and raced in every type of weather, from intense blistering heat with no shade to bitterly cold gale force wind and horizontal rain, snow and icy conditions being no exception either. But the conditions caused by the weather at the North Downs Way race were some of the worst I've experienced to run in over such a long period of time. I'm not great when it comes to running on mud and more often than not end up on my backside. After forty miles of slipping and sliding, wading through ankle deep floods over sticky mud, struggling to stay upright and failing plenty of times coupled with my inability to run over the waterlogged boggy terrain causing me to get very cold I came to the conclusion that I was not enjoying myself at all and I had absolutely no desire to put myself through any more misery, let alone another sixty miles of it. Despite the checkpoint crew's optimism saying that the conditions would be much better a few miles along, I was not convinced because the rain was relentless. They did their absolute best to encourage me to continue but my mind was made up and I dropped out of the race. It was absolutely the right decision but it didn't stop me berating myself over it. Next time, and there will be a next time, I will be better prepared mentally. Out of the total of 204 runners to start the North Downs Way 100 mile race only 110 finished with 27 runners finishing inside the magic twenty four hours. There were only 44 female starters and of those there were 19 strong women who made it to the finish line.

Having trained so hard for the triple event I couldn't help but be disappointed with myself but I had to take the positives in that I'd completed my first stage race, and my first ultra in Spain. I put the SDW100 and NDW100 into the 'Unfinished Business' file.

To end my race year I took part in the London Marathon on October 3rd and finished in four hours and nine minutes. While the London Marathon is a fantastic event, raises so much money for charity, and has over the years inspired thousands of people to get involved in running, it has almost become a victim of its own success. The size of the field of runners is such that unless you're 'up with the Kenyans' it's very crowded so you're constantly either watching that you don't clip another runner's heel, or you're looking for a gap to get through to pass slower runners. It's a very different race to what it was in the 1980's or even the early 2000's. I feel privileged to have been able to run the London Marathon eleven times, ten pre ME and one post ME, but I can't say that I will ever be entering the ballot for that one again. It is a great way to see London though, and the support is incredible.

In 2021 I ran 2056.3 miles, and 5994.9 miles since recovering from ME.

I'd spent three years since my recovery from ME working on getting my fitness back and enjoying being able to run and race again but I found myself questioning, "What now?" Age wasn't on my side but at the same time I still wanted to challenge myself. How could I get the most out of my body without breaking as I hurtle towards sixty? I decided to look into getting a coach. A good friend of mine was being coached by ultra runner Ellie Greenwood who is a top ultra runner with race wins at the iconic Western States 100 mile race and also at Comrades, amongst many others and as of writing this book, holds race course records at distances from 50 km to 100 miles. Ellie is one of the coaches at Sharman Ultra Coaching so I contacted them and within six weeks I was under the expert guidance of Ellie Greenwood. For the first time in my life I had a coach!

The thing I realised quite early on with having a coach is that it takes a huge amount of stress away from taking on a big challenge. I decided that I wanted to complete a set of races in 2022 called The Canalslam. This consisted of three ultras, each run alongside canals in England. The first was the Grand Union Canal Race (GUCR) which is the one I had to drop out of back in 2012. The race distance is 145 miles from Birmingham to Little Venice in London. The second race in the series is the Kennet and Avon Canal Race (KACR) which starts in Little Venice in London and runs 143 miles west to the city of Bristol. The final race is the Leeds Liverpool Canal Race (LLCR). Despite the name, it starts in Liverpool and is the shortest race in the series covering a mere 130 miles to Leeds. If you complete all three in the same year then, besides the three medals in a lovely presentation trophy, you are awarded the accolade of completing the Canalslam, and a year's supply of foot blister treatment (just kidding about the last bit!).

To prepare for something like that clearly takes a lot of planning. Simply working out a training schedule can be quite a task because you have to take into account how much work versus recovery the body can take. As much as I've tried to deny it, I've discovered that now I'm in my late fifties I can't run as carefree as I could when I was in my late forties, and before I became ill. So for me, training for a big challenge such as the Canalslam cannot be just a matter of running loads of miles day after day as I did in my previous incarnation as an ultra runner because that could lead to injury. Obviously we are all made differently and there are some athletes in veteran categories who can endure more stress on the body than others but I consider myself to be probably towards the top end of the normal range. So to have a coach who I can trust completely to design the training schedule specifically for me, provide advice and suggestions based on expert knowledge and experience, and monitor progress, making adjustments as and when necessary, takes away all the worry of how to prepare for a challenge as big as the one I'd set for myself. I simply say to Ellie that this is my goal and this is what I'm aiming for as the end result and Ellie would construct my training accordingly. Obviously I had to do the actual work but I don't have to worry about under or over training. The main training would be done for the first race and then in between the races it would be managed recovery at the same time as maintaining good fitness for the next race.

Although my training was fully focused on the Canalslam I did have one other race in my diary, Paul and

I had both entered the Seville Marathon, which was on 20th February 2022. I'd picked up a little knee niggle but it seemed to be improving so at two miles into the Seville Marathon I optimistically tagged on to the sub 4 hour pacer group. However, by around sixteen miles my knee niggle was complaining a little too much so I backed off the pace. It wasn't worth risking my training for the Canalslam. I finished the Maraton de Sevilla in a time of four hours and eleven minutes.

With just fifteen weeks remaining until the Grand Union Canal Race I had a short recovery from the marathon and then got my head down into some solid hard training.

PART **FOUR**

The **Canalslam**

CHAPTER 13

GUC 145 MILE RACE: EARLY HISTORY

The following is an extract taken from the Canalrace C.I.C website by kind permission of Dick Kearn.

"The 145", as it was known in its early years, was instigated in 1993 by British Waterways' Bruce Harding to promote the opening of Canal Towpaths to the public as part of their commemoration of 200 years of "Canal Mania" in Great Britain. Geoff Worsley and Harry Townsend, of the newly formed Trail Running Association, followed up the idea and proposed a non-stop race with a total time limit initially of 35 hours. (Later extended to 40 hours.)

The event was modestly promoted by word of mouth, hand-outs, and a mention in The Trailrunner newsletter of the TRA. There were to be no Checkpoints or Feedstations. Instead, runners were given a British Waterways Key and Gore-Tex Challenge[1] "Passport". The key was required to

1 The Gore-Tex Challenge involved covering the entire length of the canal over a non-specific time period. A completed passport could be returned for a commemorative brass plaque and entry into a draw for Gore-Tex products.

access BW water points and toilets, and also the rubber stamps which were used to endorse the "passport" at each of ten sites en-route, thus self-confirming completion. Competitors could have their own support crews or be self-sufficient. Twenty two competitors took up the challenge. Only Dick Kearn reached Geoff Worsley, patiently waiting at Little Venice, within the allotted time.

Despite being organised at very short notice, the event had at least proved the feasibility of a non-stop race over such a distance, but neither British Waterways nor the TRA seemed keen to repeat it. In 1996, having cut his teeth as principal organiser of Compton Harriers' 20/40 mile Challenge, and having been asked many times "Is that canal race ever going to happen again?" Dick, encouraged by his brother-in-law Phil Gadd, revived the race later that year.

Only nine runners were foolish enough to enter and only two turned up on the day! Both sadly retired near Milton Keynes, leaving Dick and Phil with time to explore possible crew meeting points and checkpoint sites for the following year.

Rod Palmer was first of four 1997 finishers from thirteen starters. Fed up with organising an event with few finishers, Dick and Phil decided to extend the overall limit to 50 hours for 1998 and 1999. This achieved its aim, but was extremely tiring for the few family and friend volunteers on which the event relied. It was decided to "split the difference" and have a forty-five hour limit. This has continued until the present day.

Before the turn of the century, word of the event had spread nationally and internationally. In the latter case mostly by the efforts of prolific ultra-runner Christian Hottas – a regular competitor from Germany, and Rory Coleman – the "Mad Brit with the Union Jack flag" having been seen at Marathon des Sables wearing a "145" t-shirt. Several MdS survivors were tempted to the canal towpath, only to fail their first attempts, and thus help build the GUCR's reputation for being much tougher than expected. The event's reputation has been further enhanced by the hard work and dedication of a few hard-core volunteers, determined to provide a good value, no nonsense, top quality race, organised by enthusiasts for enthusiasts. Long may it continue!

CHAPTER 14

THE GRAND UNION CANAL 145 MILE RACE

BIRMINGHAM TO LONDON JUNE 3–4

It was almost exactly 10 years since I last attempted this event, but this time I was going to finish, I was determined and committed. There was a solid belief inside me that I could do it, yes it would be tough, very tough, but I could be that too. I told Paul that I would start at the start line and finish at the finish line, no question.

With Ellie as my coach I felt confident in my training. I had only had one minor injury hiccup but it was totally manageable. The weeks seemed to slip by so quickly. I was getting the miles in my legs and, as far as I could, planned all the finer details for the race such as what crew points Paul would be at, what and when I would eat, my pacing, what clothing I would need, which running shoes would be best, and how to avoid or manage any potential feet issues.

During a race of this length there are numerous

things that could go wrong and it's impossible to plan for every eventuality, so I had to be as prepared as possible for everything that could be controlled. This included nutrition, clothing for all possible weather conditions and spares, medical supplies for fixing feet issues or wounds, facial wipes to freshen up when tiredness takes over, spare socks, spare shoes, and (remembering my last attempt) spare glasses. There is also a list of essential requirements that I had to have for health and safety reasons, most of the time though these requirements are just a matter of common sense to ensure that you don't put your or indeed anyone else's life or safety at risk.

With my coach's advice I'd settled on a run/walk plan that I would try and stick to for as long as possible. It was mainly about two things, firstly conserving energy in the first half to help me through the second half to the finish, and secondly, and equally as important, consuming a minimum of 200 calories per hour to keep my energy stores from totally depleting. So the weekend before the race Paul and I sat down with the maps and worked out estimated times that I would be at the crew points plus noting what nutrition I might need and when. It all looked great on paper and if it had gone to that plan I would be at the GUCR Finish Line sometime between 7pm and 9pm on Saturday.

At 4am on Friday 3rd June my alarm went off. I had laid out all my kit the night before so I methodically got myself organised. With 20 minutes to go we left the hotel room and strolled to the start in Gas Street, Birmingham. I was feeling reasonably calm and relaxed but quite keen to get going so I wouldn't have to worry about anything else other than keeping to the plan and getting to the finish. We were all called to make our way down to the Start Line by the canal and after a few words from one of the Race Directors the countdown from five started. Four, three, two, one, and at precisely 6am we were off. After the months and months of training it was a relief to finally be running the event that I'd been training for, although I had to keep distracting myself from the full daunting distance ahead of me. As most of the field disappeared off along the trail ahead I had to focus hard on keeping to my planned easy pace with a repeated 20 minute run and 10 minute walk. My vest pack was loaded with everything I would need until I saw Paul at the first checkpoint at 10.7 miles. I was eating and drinking well, so far so good.

CP1 and Crew point 1 Solihull (10.7 miles)
Estimated arrival time 8.30am
Actual arrival time 8.20am, departure 8.27am
Total stopped time 7 minutes

Between CP1 and the next crew point there was a section of deep sticky mud which was unavoidable. The wet mud engulfed my trail shoes and I made a rash decision to change my shoes and socks at the next crew point because I knew if my feet got wet then it would cause blisters and I couldn't afford that to happen this early in the race. But when I took my shoes and socks off my feet were dry so I just changed my socks and kept to my trail shoes. This turned out to be a wise decision. All good, still thinking straight!

Crew point 2 Warwick (18.1 miles)

Estimated arrival time 10.30am
Actual arrival time 10.07am, departure 10.13am
Cumulative stopped time 13 minutes

The third crew point at 30 miles went like clockwork, I had a pre-ordered peanut butter and jam sandwich, swapped over my vest pack for a restocked one, picked up my detour notes which I would need to navigate around a closed section of towpath four miles ahead, and went on my way.

Crew point 3 Leamington Spa (30 miles)
Estimated arrival time 1.30pm
Actual arrival time 12.46pm, departure 12.53
Cumulative stopped time 20 minutes

At this point I have to say that at best I have an incredibly poor sense of direction and despite having a reasonably clear map of the diversion, after about five minutes I started to panic thinking I'd taken the wrong road. So I stopped a family who were out walking and showed them my map asking if I was on the correct road. To make matters worse they didn't recognise any of the roads at all! My heart sank, how could I get so lost so quickly? Suddenly I realised that I was looking at the wrong side of the paper and I was showing them the map of the diversion at 136 miles. It's not surprising that they didn't recognise it. Turning it over they immediately identified the roads and said I was fine and directed me further. I was so very happy to make it back to the familiarity of the canal.

I breezed through the official CP3 at thirty six miles

and continued on to see Paul at the forty one mile crew point. There is a saying in ultra running circles of 'Beware The Chair'. There was a chair and I had a nice mug of soup waiting for me, so I slumped my body in the chair and sat to drink while Paul refuelled my vest pack. It had become quite cold and I was enjoying the break with a hot drink a little too much. But my comforting pea and mint soup was in an insulated mug so I couldn't even warm my hands around it although it was good to get warm on the inside. Revitalised and with another layer of clothing on and a refuelled pack I was on my way again. Despite how I felt inside, Paul recorded notes on his phone saying that I "looked strong".

Crew point 4 Rugby (41.4 miles)
Estimated arrival time 4pm
Actual arrival time 3.43pm, departure 3.54pm
Cumulative stopped time 31 minutes

It was somewhere around fifty miles into the race that I started to have some stomach issues and nausea so I tried to let my stomach settle before I put anything else in. The need for bathroom breaks became a bit of a frequent nuisance and ate into my time and this is where the plan started to slide. The next crew point was at CP4 and I remembered that Paul was going to have a pot noodle meal ready for me, yummy! I hoped he would make the red tomato flavoured one and not the white creamy one, which I instinctively knew that my stomach would not tolerate. It was indeed the red one with fusilli pasta, and I sat down once again in the sinful chair enjoying another break without too much regard for the ticking clock.

CP4 and Crew point 5 Northampton (53.1 miles)
Estimated arrival time 7pm
Actual arrival time 6.45pm, departure time 7.10pm
Cumulative stopped time 56 minutes

Even though I had applied extensive anti chafing cream at the start and earlier in the day, due to the all too frequent bathroom stops I was suffering from chafing in some quite sensitive places which was becoming very sore. I had reapplied cream but it was too late to stop it being fairly uncomfortable for the remaining ninety two miles of the race, and beyond. There are more hazards in ultra running than some people realise!

It would be dusk by the time I got to the next crew point so I'd picked up my head torch and hi-viz in preparation for the night running to come.

The nausea was still coming in waves and by the time I got to the next crew point even though just the thought of food turned my stomach, I knew I needed to eat something. I forced in some Pringles and Jaffa cakes and struggled out of my sweaty shorts and short sleeve top and into leggings and a long sleeve top which would keep me warmer through the night hours. I also changed out of my trail shoes into my spare running shoes, which after over 60 miles in the trails, almost felt like comfy slippers. Feeling much more comfortable wearing a warmer kit in the cold night air I left the crew point and went out into the dark night.

Crew point 6 Blisworth (62.5 miles)
Estimated arrival time 9.30pm

Actual arrival time 9.50pm, departure 10.12pm
Cumulative stopped time 1 hour and 18 minutes

The next one and a half miles were away from the canal, mostly along a main road and over the Blisworth Tunnel. I was wearing hi-viz and had my head torch on but it was very dark and there were no street lights. To make matters worse, very occasionally a car would drive towards me with its bright headlights negating the light from my head torch. I became confused, I couldn't see any head torches ahead of me so I panicked again. I stopped and sent Paul a Whatsapp message saying "LOST ALREADY!" Thankfully he wasn't too far away and drove to the point where I would need to turn off the road onto the trail leading back to the towpath. I ran towards the tail lights in the distance, hugely relieved to make out the shape of Paul's pick-up truck as I got closer. With my navigational challenges in the darkness, on my own, I'm almost certain that I would have missed the turn onto the trail path. Directed off the road and back onto the canal towpath I relaxed again and got back into my stride. I tried to push away the thoughts that I wasn't even half way yet, exchanging them for the words of my coach "Relentless Forward Progress".

At the next crew point there was a hot chocolate waiting for me. Sinking into the chair with my hot chocolate comforting me on the inside I lost all sense of time and urgency. The tiredness was setting in. I was only at the halfway point and the sands of time were slipping away.

Crew point 7 Milton Keynes (72.3 miles)
Estimated arrival time midnight

Actual arrival time 00.50, departure 1.10am
Cumulative stopped time 1 hour and 38 minutes

With continuing stomach issues still causing frequent bathroom stops and nausea I pushed on into the night. As it was well into the summer months I reminded myself that the night would be short and told myself that I would feel much better when the sun came up in a few hours time.

One of the most, if not the most important things to have in long distance ultra running is a very strong 'Why'. It's the reason why you keep going when every fibre in your body wants to stop. The body's own intrinsic self-preservation instinct along with the mind's strong powers of persuasion will come up with all kinds of very convincing reasons to stop what you're doing, and have a lie down if the natural balance of homeostasis is threatened. The reason why you continue through the pain cave and on to the finish line has to be much stronger than the mind's reasons to stop. As I ran-walked alongside the canal I thought about why, why was I here, cold and lonely alongside a canal in the dark, 75 miles into a 145 mile race when I could be tucked up in a nice warm bed, why did I think this was a good idea, what on earth possessed me to enter this in the first place? Then I remembered. I like to challenge myself to feel alive and for a long time that was taken away from me, and that felt much worse than how I was feeling in that moment. This book was also one of those Whys. I wanted it to be something that would pass on the message of no matter what life throws at you, never give up. So with that in mind, my thoughts turned to how could I write a book with that message if I listened to my mind and gave up in the first race of the Slam? I thought of my grandchildren too, I wanted them to be proud of their Nana and to read the book in the future and maybe push their own limits. I thought of my own grown up children and despite, or maybe because of the issues I've had with my two daughters over the years, I still wanted to be a strong example to them. I thought about my Coach, Ellie, and the belief she has in me after all the work we have put into getting my body ready for this challenge. I found a new determination and quietened the voices in my head telling me to stop. I was going to get this done.

Crew point 8 Milton Keynes (80.4 miles)
Estimated arrival time 2am
Actual arrival time 3.45am, departure 4.05am
Cumulative stopped time 1 hour and 58 minutes

Having had a hot cup of herbal tea at the crew point and with the grey daylight slowly replacing the darkness I went on my way, but within a few minutes of leaving the crew point I had to turn and run back. My Garmin watch had a blank screen, the battery had died three hours prematurely after only 22 hours! I had a backup Garmin in the truck and called Paul so as to catch him before he left for the next crew point. As I ran back Paul ran out to meet me, I gave him the dead one and he gave me my trusty old back up. I have a fondness for this Garmin, it was a big statement purchase when I recovered from ME indicating I was on my way back. It had been with me from the start of my road back to ultra running, from the Couch to 5k schedule, to 10ks, marathons and ultras, through thousands of miles up to a certain training run out on the trails in the Andalusian hills where I had a car drive into me, the bonnet forcing me into a ditch and then they just drove off. I ended up with a few cuts and bruises but my Garmin suffered worse, there was a crack right across its face. I was pretty upset. So my Garmin went into semi-retirement and I bought a shiny new one with a much longer battery life, supposedly 25 hours, to go with my longer events. But on this day it let me down three hours too soon. By this time the numbers didn't mean too much to me. The average pace seemed slow but I was banking on the quicker miles covered earlier in the race saved on the first garmin to bring the average pace down a bit. Clearly I wasn't aware of how much time I had wasted.

Crew point 9 Leighton Buzzard (87 miles)
Estimated arrival time 3.30am
Actual arrival time 6.15am, departure 6.40
Cumulative stopped time 2 hours and 23 minutes

By the time I got to crew point 9 I had been awake for over 26 hours and had been running and walking for over 24 of those, and despite the serotonin releasing daylight I felt so very tired. Paul suggested a ten minute nap and I didn't argue. I closed my eyes and I was instantly sleeping. I'd heard of ultra runners having ten or even five minute sleeps before but never believed I would be able to fall asleep so quickly. So when Paul woke me after my allotted ten minutes from what felt like a deep sleep I was amazed at how refreshed I felt. I was now past the point where I had dropped out of this race 10 years previously. I was much quicker back then and I'd got to mile 85 in the very early hours of the morning when it was still very dark. The weather that night was wild, bitterly cold and pouring with rain. I had been running just behind another runner, both of us head down against the elements. Suddenly the runner in front stopped dead and I crashed into the back of him. He had apparently run into an overhanging branch and I hadn't seen him stop. We readjusted ourselves and trudged on but it wasn't long before I knew something was not right. I realised that I couldn't see very well and when I checked my glasses I discovered that one lens of my varifocals was missing. It must have popped out when I crashed into my fellow runner. I continued for a mile or two but running in the dark next to a canal with impaired vision became too unsafe for me so I decided to DNF (Did Not Finish) at about mile 85, CP6. That's the reason why I made doubly sure that I included a spare pair of glasses when I was packing for this event.

My stomach was still being very picky about what it would allow me to put in and Paul was sending me messages trying to tempt me with anything from a mocha coffee to slices of pizza. I do like a nice coffee but at that point in time it was a definite no however pizza was a definite maybe so I risked it. I clearly wasn't getting enough calories in but what I did eat I kept down, and that was the main thing. I just needed more. My back up trusty Garmin with a cracked face was also now empty so I swapped back to my partly charged Fenix.

Crew point 10 Slapton (94.2 miles)
Estimated arrival time 6am

Actual arrival time 8.45am, departure 9.10am
Cumulative stopped time 2 hours and 48 minutes

The grey day didn't give me the lift I needed and I felt heavy with tiredness. The more tired I became the more confused my brain was and I started to send Paul live location pins to confirm I was on course, and also to give him an idea of how slow I'd become so he would know when to expect me at the next crew point. Paul would reply with a calm and encouraging message but all the time he was becoming more and more concerned that I was going to run out of time to get to the finish before the final cut off. Just past 101 miles, at bridge 135, which was only two bridges away from the next crew point, I had to sit down on some steps because I was hallucinating. I kept seeing dogs that weren't there, one was actually standing on top of the water in the canal. It didn't frighten me, it just added to my confusion. A minute or two later I got my mind back on what I was doing and pushed on the crew point. While waiting for me to arrive Paul recorded another note on his phone, ending with "on the home straight", if only that was the case!

Crew point 11 Tring (102.5 miles)
Estimated arrival time 7.30am
Actual arrival time 11.55am, departure 12.18pm
Cumulative stopped time 3 hours and 11 minutes

I'd had another 10 minute sleep at the crew point, as did another runner who I'd spent some time running with and chatting to earlier in the race. When I was with her earlier, if you had looked at both of us and been asked which one of us was more likely to finish, I'm pretty sure you would have said the other runner. She looked strong and as if she could keep going at a good pace for many more hours to come. But I was surprised and sad to discover that shortly after the crew point she DNF'd.

Obviously all of my previously carefully worked out estimated arrival times were now just a work of fiction and I needed new and more urgent target times if I stood any chance of finishing inside the final cut off time, and indeed inside the check point cut offs leading up to it. When I saw Paul at the next crew point he took on a serious tone and told me that to make the 7pm cut off at CP8 I would have to leave the next three crew points by 2.50pm, 4pm, and 5pm respectively. Taking into consideration the re-fuelling of my pack and dealing with anything else that may have come up it meant that I would need to arrive at those crew points at the very least five minutes before those times. Now the race was really on.

Crew point 12 Hemel Hempstead (108.5 miles)
Original estimated arrival time 9am, actual arrival time 2.32pm
Departure target 2.50pm, actual departure 2.40pm
Cumulative stopped time 3 hours and 19 minutes

In the planning notes I'd anticipated enjoying coffee and cake at crew point 12, and then a veggie wrap at the 123 mile point, with various snacks in between, which all sounds rather nice and civilised. But the food plan was well and truly out of the window by now and I was just doing my best to get something in that my body could both tolerate and work with to help me to keep going. Later on this included banana, jaffa cakes, pringles and coke, but all I could manage at this stage was a few sips of pea and mint soup. It was not the most calorific or nutritious of foods but I was working a careful balancing act between eating something that didn't make the nausea worse and a complete energy deficit if I threw up any calories I had managed to consume.

Crew point 13 Watford (115 miles)
Original estimated arrival time 11am, actual arrival time 4.54pm
Departure target 5pm, actual departure 5.14pm
Cumulative stopped time 3 hours and 39 minutes

This was over ten miles more than the furthest distance I'd ever covered in one go, but I still had another thirty miles ahead of me. There are things that I *know* about what was happening at this stage, such as the fact that I had a change of clothes, fresh socks and a refreshing face wipe, and that I was desperately trying to ignore the ongoing chafing issue in the very sensitive area, but there is not a lot that I can remember about anything else around this time. Clearly my memory bank was taking some time out, and who can blame it.

I also know that I was hallucinating frequently. One theory is that hallucinations or illusions can happen when the brain gets to a point where it's so tired that it cannot accurately interpret the vision so it kind of guesses what the particular vision or shape is, often getting it wrong.

To begin with I found it quite novel. Having heard about similar experiences of other ultra runners' hallucinations I thought, hey cool I'm now a member of that club, but I soon became very fed up of seeing lots of different animals large and small on the towpath ahead of me only to realise that it was hedgerow, a tree, or a pile of kit belonging to a canal boat owner.

Walking had become the new running but I was in danger of being timed out at CP8 so I was alternating fast walking with a zombie shuffle run. Hot spots on my feet were an indication that blisters were forming and I was reminded of something my coach told me that foot issues were one of the main reasons for dropping out of a race. I couldn't afford to let that happen so I contacted Paul to ask him to get out the medical box and be ready to fix my feet. The perks of crewing an ultra runner!

CP8 and Crew point 14 Rickmansworth (120.3 miles)
Original estimated arrival time 12.15pm, actual arrival time 6.45pm
Departure target 7pm, actual departure 7.10pm
Cumulative stopped time 4 hours and 04 minutes

I was so relieved to have made the 7pm cut off at CP8 and as I sat in the chair calmly drinking a cup of coke I remember saying "Now I can relax a bit". I was clearly delirious because that sounds hilarious now, and I can still see the faces of the checkpoint crew as they were packing up, looking somewhat surprised to hear me say that I had time to "relax".

I had just under five hours to cover the thirteen miles

to CP9 before it closed at midnight. That may sound like plenty of time but the truth of it is, at the pace I was moving by that time meant that I was right on the wire so Paul urged me on so he could fix my feet and send me on my way. As I peeled off my socks the sight was not a pretty one, my feet had some big blisters. But there was no time to waste, I did the needle work to relieve the pressure and Paul taped them up. With another change of socks and back into my trail shoes I was moving again. It was just three miles until I would next see Paul and I received a Whatsapp message from him midway saying,

"I'm at bridge 80 with pizza",

That can't be right I thought, maybe I've missed a turn. So I stopped and checked my map, and trying desperately to stay calm I replied "Do you mean 180?"

"Oh yes, sorry" he said.

Crew point 15 Uxbridge (123 miles)
Original estimated arrival time 1pm
Actual arrival time 8pm, departure 8.20pm
Cumulative stopped time 4 hours and 24 minutes

There are ultra runners who can eat all kinds of foods during very long events, and I have to admit that I'm quite jealous of them because as we've already established, my digestive system is much more temperamental. I forced myself to eat two slices of pizza and tried to ignore what my stomach was suddenly telling me. I refocused and knew that I just had to get through five more miles by myself and then Paul would be running/walking alongside me to the finish line. I'd been alone in my own head for far too long and I was looking forward to having a much more positive conversation. Even though I was completely determined to finish, I felt that having Paul with me for the last seventeen or so miles would absolutely guarantee it. I'd lost all judgement of space and time by now though so I sent Paul a live location pin to give him an idea of where I was and how long I was likely to be. I actually laughed out loud when he replied by sending me his live location pin, what use was that to me? I barely knew where I was let alone work out his position in relation to that. But then he said "I'm at bridge 190. I think I have everything we will need to get to the finish, including your spare glasses and Garmin". What I actually needed though was a spare pair of legs.

Crew point 16 Cowley (127.5 miles)
Original estimated arrival time 2.30pm
Actual arrival time 10pm, departure – immediately!
Cumulative stopped time 4 hours and 24 minutes

There was one more checkpoint cut off to meet and then the final cut off. I had two hours to cover five and a half miles, and then a further three hours to cover the final twelve miles. It was going to be tight. A brisk walking pace would probably do it, but there was nothing brisk about my walking pace after 127 miles. Remarkably Paul didn't realise this and all I could do was watch as he strode off. Noticing that I was not with him he stopped and waited in silence. I had been so looking forward to having him with me for support and encouragement and it wasn't supposed to be like this. My mood suddenly dropped and I told Paul that this was not how I had imagined it would be. This was a bit of a wake up call for him and I think he must have realised that the person I was after having covered almost 130 miles on foot was not the normal person he knows me as, I was well and truly in survival mode. From there he took my hand, we walked together, and he supported and encouraged me through every mile we covered together. I felt a shift, I didn't need to worry about anything anymore. Everything was going to work out. My Garmin died yet again, but I switched back to my trusted spare. We made it to the last checkpoint at 11.45, just fifteen minutes before it closed. So with three hours and fifteen minutes to get to the finish line, there was no time to stop. One of the checkpoint crew said I would need to average 16.30 minute miles to make it. I hadn't managed that pace for a while so the only way I was going to get anywhere near achieving that was to run. I decided on a one minute run in every mile but the first mile came in just over sixteen minutes and that felt just too close to the margin. So it became a 90 second run in every mile, and that worked much better with the pacing. However each time the mile came around I had to grit my teeth and push myself with all I had to break into something resembling a run. I have never been more 'in the moment' as I was during those 90 painful gut wrenching seconds. It was raining, and the rain was becoming heavier. I was thankful that Paul had checked out the course on his bike a week or so before because I didn't need to think about which way to go. I could just be guided by Paul and put all my focus on getting to the finish line at Little Venice.

The countdown was on with just 4 miles to go, then 3, 2, and I was finally inside the last mile. I so yearned to see the lights of the finish but the path bended this way and that and I couldn't see far enough ahead. I was running, actually running. But this running was on pure adrenaline because there was nothing left in my legs. I'd left Paul behind me but I was shouting to him "Where is it? Where is it?!" But all he would say was to "keep going straight, it's not far now".

Finally, I could see a small light in the distance and as I got closer I could hear people clapping. I'd made it and I've never been so happy to see a finish line!

Estimated finish time – between 7pm and 10pm Saturday
Actual finish time 2.51am Sunday
Overall cumulative stopped time 4 hours and 24 minutes

Total time 44 hours 51 minutes
53rd place out of 53 finishers (45 dropped out)

But a finish is a finish and that was always the main goal. It also leaves room for a PB at the next one.

At 3am we called an Uber to get back to the truck and decided to have a couple hours of sleep before attempting the two hour drive home; especially as Paul hadn't got much sleep over the past two days either. I don't have any recollection of getting into the truck and going to sleep, but I do remember waking up desperate for a wee. The rain by now was torrential and we were in a deserted area parked next to some waste land so I decided to squat just by the truck. The sky had a hint of dawn breaking through but there was no one around. I got my trousers and underwear down and went to squat. What was I thinking! My legs were having none of it, squatting requires quadriceps strength and my quads were mashed and had very little strength left in them, certainly not enough to squat. My legs gave way and as I tried to regain my balance I stepped further and further back, ultimately landing on my bare bottom within a big area of nettles and stingers. I couldn't even put my hands down as I was surrounded by spiky weeds. For some crazy reason I didn't want Paul, my husband of eight years, to see me in such an undignified state but I had no choice. I shouted to him praying that he would hear me inside the truck. He came to my rescue immediately, grabbed my hands and tried to pull me up, but I had no purchase on the ground so he was pulling my full weight. It took some time but he finally heaved me into an upright position. I made myself decent and got back into the truck with a scratched and stung backside and some thorns to deal with later. Together in the truck we laughed and laughed, and still do when we remember that finale to the weekend.

CHAPTER 15

THE KENNET AND AVON CANAL 145 MILE RACE

LONDON TO BRISTOL JULY 22–23

Seventeen days before race day I was out on a twelve mile training run in Spain. It was very hot and I was inside the last mile looking forward to a nice long cold drink that was waiting for me in a cool bag back at the car. Then suddenly I was flying through the air and landed heavily on the front and side of my face. I think my head hit the ground so hard that it actually bounced off the pavement. I lifted my head up and there was blood all over my hands. I couldn't see the cut and couldn't work out where the blood was coming from until I saw it dripping down from my head. There was already a large pool of blood on the pavement and I laid there watching the traffic drive past wondering what I should do and why no one was stopping to help me. But within a couple of minutes two Spanish men came running over and then a car did stop and a woman also came rushing over. Shortly after a police car pulled up behind her car and the Police Officer came over to assist. While the woman tended to my head trying to stem the flow of blood, the men were on the phone calling an ambulance. I can speak some Spanish but I was in shock so I couldn't follow everything that was going on around me. I had managed to stop the distance and time recording on my watch though and remember feeling a bit annoyed that I'd only got 11.26 miles instead of the intended 12. I was clearly in a state of shock, dazed and confused, and also emotional. A couple of hours later I was heading home with Paul having been patched up at the hospital although I was still bleeding from my head. The headache continued for a few days and my right eye and side of my face changed colours daily leading all the way up to race day.

To avoid the panicked chasing of checkpoint cut off times that made the end of the GUCR so stressful I knew that I had to be tougher. I could not afford to languish around at crew points, especially the early ones when it feels like I have plenty of time. I had learnt that lesson the hard way and I was determined that I would have a much less stressful finish to this race. I'd had lengthy conversations with my coach and also with Paul and made a few changes to the race strategy that I'd set at GUCR. Firstly, there would be no sitting in a chair at crew points until at the very least half way. I needed to be in and out of crew points as efficiently as a Formula One pit stop. I also made adjustments with my nutrition in the hope of avoiding the stomach issues that I'd suffered in GUCR. During a long training run I had experimented with liquid meals which contained 500 calories and all the nutrients you needed in a main meal, and critically my stomach seemed to approve so I included a couple of bottles of the liquid meal in my food store for the race.

I felt confident going into the second event mainly because I had proved to myself that I can cover the distance, but also because my recovery had gone really well and I felt that I'd built strength from the first race. Obviously it wasn't going to be easy, running these kinds of distances are never easy, and at some point it would hurt, and I would get tired, and my body would scream at me to stop, but I'd been through all that before and I was determined to get through it again.

It was the same routine as last time, kit laid out the night before, early night and alarm set for 4am. Everything went smoothly and as we walked to the start Paul recorded the first note on his phone; "Walking to the start on a grey grey, but thankfully dry London morning, and the word from Trin is 'I am going to start at the start and finish at the finish, just like last time' ". While waiting at Little Venice in London mingling with friends old and new ready for the 6am send-off I remembered how I felt the last time I was there at the end of GUCR, and I felt okay knowing that I was about to put my body through it all again.

The first section up to checkpoint one followed the last section of the GUCR in reverse although it all looked quite different in daylight. I adopted the same pacing as before with a twenty minute run and ten minute walk feeling really comfortable. I ran straight through CP1 and on to the first crew point where I would meet Paul. With the experience of GUCR and remembering how much time I let slip through during crew points, I wanted to be as efficient as I could be during this race, particularly during the first half. So when I saw Paul it needed to be a case of just swapping empty bottles for full ones, refilling the pockets in my vest pack with gels and snacks and then moving on quickly.

Crew point 1 Hayes (13.5 miles)
Estimated arrival time 9.25am
Actual arrival time 8.49am, departure 8.52am
Cumulative stopped time 3 minutes

While running well within my comfort zone I had still made good time but it would become apparent that the first section was the easiest part of the course. The ground would become more uneven and rocky the further along we got. Added to that there would be long stretches where we would be fighting our way through very overgrown paths with huge leaves blocking our way from both sides. It was literally a jungle out there. But at this point I was blissfully unaware of what lay ahead.

The early checkpoint cut off times are reasonably tight given the length of the race but they do allow for runners to slow down in the second half of the race. So it was a careful balancing act in the first half, being mindful of the cut off times but also conserving as much energy as possible for later on in the race. Check Point 2 would close at 12.30pm and with my estimated arrival time of midday it only gave me a 30 minute cushion. Sometimes the shorter the cushion time early on means the less likely you'll make the cut off times in the latter stages so I had to be careful of pacing my energy but at the same time moving fast enough to stay well inside time limits, at least until the halfway mark.

CP2 and crew point 2 Maidenhead (26.9 miles)
Estimated arrival time Midday
Actual arrival time 11.46am, departure 11.52am
Cumulative stopped time 9 minutes

Although I've completely recovered from ME, it did leave me with anxiety issues and I have had to learn how to deal with the onset of an anxiety attack before it gets out of control. Little concerns during a race, such as taking a wrong turn or getting too close to a cut off time could cause me to have a major panic if I didn't act as soon as I felt the first signs of anxiety. Deep slow breathing, positive reassuring self-talk and just stopping for a few minutes to bring myself to a place of calm have all been tools that I have used both during my training and racing ultra events. I also use Rescue Remedy from the Bach Flower Remedies especially when I'm going into a situation that could be stressful and I have found it to be really helpful, so there was a little bottle of Rescue Remedy in my medical box.

Crew point 3 Marlow (35.2 miles)
Estimated arrival time 2.10pm
Actual arrival time 1.52pm, departure 1.58pm
Cumulative stopped time 15 minutes

The weather up until now had been almost perfect and during the next stage there was some light rain which was nice and refreshing. But then the sky clouded over with a big dark heavy greyness and suddenly the light refreshing shower became a torrential downpour. I pulled out my jacket from the back of my vest pack and put it on as quickly as I could. I couldn't tell how long the rain would last but I knew if I got drenched I would be dealing with other problems later on such as blisters and chafing. As it turned out the rain stopped as quickly as it started and it was suddenly very warm, so the jacket was off and back in my pack. The miles were ticking over nicely and by the next crew point there would be less than a hundred miles to go which was a good mental milestone.

Crew point 4 Shiplake (46.7 miles)
Estimated arrival time 5pm
Actual arrival time 4.52pm, departure 5.02pm
Cumulative stopped time 25 minutes

Paul was waiting for me at the crew point with a cup of herbal tea and a tube of Pringles, both gratefully received. I was beginning to feel like I didn't want any more gels so I needed to keep my carbohydrate intake up with food, which was easier said than done with my temperamental stomach. Now being 'within a hundred miles of the finish' did not prove to be as comforting a thought as I had hoped for! Paul continued to record notes on his phone and the difference between how I looked and how I felt is remarkable. Paul's recording says "Trin looks happier now, more positive and determined after her cup of tea". It could be that he was also crewing for someone else who was displaying all those attributes and getting us mixed up because I may have been determined but not so sure that I radiated happiness and positivity at that point.

Crew point 5 Theale (59 miles)
Estimated arrival time 8.30pm
Actual arrival time 8.21pm, departure 8.35pm
Cumulative stopped time 39 minutes

It's very easy to make rules about what I will and won't do when the going gets tough, but not always so easy to stick to those rules. I was still about fifteen miles from the halfway mark but I couldn't help myself. I sat down! My mind was doing a little victory dance and my legs were blissfully happy. Consequently this is where the time started to slip, I had given in already. But despite that, I still knew that I wouldn't be completely beaten, I had just made it a little harder.

I had planned a hot meal in a pot for this stop but the macaroni cheese didn't even make it past my lips, just the smell of it was enough to start me retching! So instead I had a replacement meal drink, which contained a precious 500 calories and enough carbs to keep me moving for a while. Chafing was starting to become a problem again, despite the changes I'd made after suffering at GUCR. I would definitely have to review this again before the last event. It's surprising how the minutes slip by so easily because by the time I'd refuelled and replaced empty bottles for full ones in my vest pack 14 minutes had already passed. I needed to get myself moving so I put on my head torch ready for the dark night time hours ahead.

CP5 and crew point 6 Thatcham (70 miles)
Estimated arrival time 11.10pm
Actual arrival time 11.39pm, departure 11.59pm
Cumulative stopped time 59 minutes

Paul is waiting for me with a hot chocolate and now my resolve has been broken I take the opportunity to sit while I drink it. The sugar picks me up a little but I feel tired and sluggish. I'm going into the toughest part of the race, and with 70 miles behind me I'm still not even halfway. As I leave the crew point Paul records a note saying "Refuelled and looking good, heading into the graveyard shift but in better shape than last time". It's dark, cold and lonely. My body and my mind are so tired and are craving sleep. But I have been through this before and know that I have to keep moving forward. I somehow get myself lost in Newbury and my tired and confused brain cannot work out the map, although it has to be said that even awake and alert I still struggle with maps. I call Paul and send him a location pin in the hope that he can put me back on course. There is a group of drunk teenagers hanging around and I feel vulnerable for a while but after retracing my steps I'm finally back on the correct route and running again.

The next couple of hours are very lonely. The hallucinations were back again and they provided some interesting distraction. I'm run/walking alongside the canal in the deep darkness of the night with only the beam of my head torch lighting the way. There's not a soul around and my mind starts to imagine all kinds of different scenarios. What if I'm attacked by someone hiding out here, how long before someone realised, would anyone ever find me, or find my body. With so many incidents of such tragic events on the news my mind had plenty of references to play with so I just tried to keep breaking into the train of thought with something more positive. I was very pleased to see Paul at an unscheduled stop near Hungerford and decided to take a 10 minute nap. That helped to reset my mind and my mood and I continued on to the next scheduled stop at CP6.

CP6 and crew point 7 Marlborough (83.4 miles)
Estimated arrival time 3am Saturday
Actual arrival time 5.15am, departure 5.33am
Cumulative stopped time 1 hour and 17 minutes

Even though I'm in a slightly better position at this point of the race than I was at the same point at GUCR I have still lost a lot of time. Apart from spending time at crew points, and getting lost in Newbury, extra time was added on the canal path during sections of it that were completely overgrown to the point where you couldn't see where to put your feet on the rutted trail. The front runners possibly skipped through these sections but for me it was unrunnable. This and my tiredness and despair through the night possibly made the estimated times to crew points too optimistic. But it was the beginning of a new day and as dawn became daylight my serotonin level increased and I started to feel more awake. I put on a fresh pair of socks, had my morning cup of herbal tea accompanied with as many Jaffa cakes as I could manage while Paul restocked my vest pack and then sent me on my way again. As I continued to fight my way through the overgrown canal path I concluded that this must be the most pedestrian unfriendly canal path that I have ever run on, and through the years different races have taken me alongside a lot of canal paths! It would be impossible for instance to push a wheelchair or pushchair though long sections of the walking route and I even saw cyclists having problems getting their bikes through. The suggested race kit list could definitely have included a machete, although it's probably not a good idea to run with one. As the minutes and hours slipped away I started to worry about cut off times, a familiar territory that I did not want to revisit.

Crew point 8 Pewsey (94.5 miles)
Estimated arrival time 6.20am
Actual arrival time 9.13am, departure 9.21am
Cumulative stopped time 1 hour and 25 minutes

The uneven rocky ground had taken its toll on my feet and the sharp rocks stabbed into the sole of my trail shoes with every step shooting pain messages to my brain telling me to stop. I had to ignore the pain and put my focus elsewhere, stopping was not an option. Chafing in unmentionable areas was also making me wince but it had got to a point where it didn't feel like it could get any worse so I decided to ignore that too. I knew in the back of my mind that I still had over twelve hours of run/walking ahead of me and that seemed like an awfully long time, so I also filed that in the 'To ignore' section. The challenge was to ignore everything that was pulling me down and to focus on anything positive. This was not an easy thing to do at 100 miles into a 145 mile race but if you look hard enough there is always something positive. In the years that I was ill with ME I had dreams in which I was running and feeling free and happy only to wake up to reality. But my dreams did eventually come true, and that was something I could hold on to at times like this when it felt tough.

Paul met me at 104 miles, another unscheduled stop, to try and pick me up a bit. He takes a look at my feet and does what he can to make them feel a little more comfortable. I have another change of socks and push on. I'm now heading to Caen Locks, the only real hill on the route and thankfully we are descending. At the top of the hill I take the wrong path but realise quite quickly when I can see where I should be running on the other side of a hedge, so I back track and am suddenly faced with the magnificent sight of the locks descending into the distance. There are 29 locks in all descending 237 feet in 2 miles (1 in 44 gradient). They were opened in 1810 and are well worth a visit. At the top of the locks is a cafe and that was where I was meeting Paul for crew point 9.

Crew point 9 Devizes (107.9 miles)
Estimated arrival time 10.30am
Actual arrival time 1.45pm, departure 2.05pm
Cumulative stopped time 1 hour and 45 minutes

My original plan was to have breakfast from the cafe at this crew point but breakfast time had long since passed, it was even too late for brunch so this became a lunch stop instead. My stomach was not happy to receive food by now and the very dry veggie sausage in a very dry bap was not easy to consume, even with a lukewarm mocha to wash it down with. I did have a little more success with half a buttered teacake though. I was keen not to stop for too long so I used the bathroom and started on the descent. I'm constantly pushing away the negative thoughts and trying to focus on getting to the next checkpoint and then the next crew point. Paul meets me at 113.5 miles to top up my water bottle but I don't stop, there's no time. The next crew point was just over the 120 mile point and I was really struggling to keep moving so Paul walked down the canal path to meet me. There were some public benches and I was so desperately tired. I lay down on one of the wooden park benches and instantly fell asleep. Paul woke me after 10 minutes and a little revived, we walked on to the next crew point.

Crew point 10 Bradford-on-Avon (120.4 miles)
Estimated arrival time 2.40pm
Actual arrival time 18.15pm, departure 18.15pm, no time to stop
Cumulative stopped time 1 hour and 45 minutes

I was making good progress and then about a mile from the next crew point where Paul would be joining me for the remainder of the route, I suddenly felt a flash of fire in the ball of my foot. I could only imagine what had happened but I tried not to. I messaged Paul saying that I needed the first aid box as soon as possible and he ran back down the towpath to meet me. As I peeled off my sock I prepared myself for a nasty sight but although my foot was angry red it didn't look anywhere near as bad as it felt. Paul padded it with natural soft wool and put one fresh sock on. I had no reason to look at my other foot so I didn't waste any more time and we carried on together. The padding did help but it wasn't long before both of my feet were burning.

CP9 Bath (130.5 miles)
Estimated arrival time 5.50pm
Actual arrival time 10pm, departure 10.05pm
Cumulative stopped time 1 hour and 50 minutes

I arrived at CP9 one hour before the cut off time so nowhere near as tight as it was at the final checkpoint in GUCR. I felt positive and motivated. Even though I knew that I was way behind my planned finishing time, I was sure that I would at least achieve a personal best time for the distance, and by quite a decent margin. There were a few runners around us so I also knew I had a chance of not being the last one to finish like I was the last time. The marshal at the checkpoint warned us that the route got a little tricky from there to the finish so we needed to take care following the map. I had Paul with me, and maps are his thing so I didn't worry too much. We calculated that even a slow pace of 20 minute miles would get me to the finish at around 2am and the race didn't close until 3am. With this in mind I felt confident, and the pain in my feet and tiredness in my body was briefly forgotten. We decided on a 90 second run in every mile as it had worked well during the same stage in GUCR. We continued with this pace pattern until my feet started to scream at me again. The route had indeed become a little tricky, and had deteriorated into a barely discernible track along the river and through cow fields. The pace dropped as we tried to navigate our way through the fields on rutted ground. I became stressed and irritated, and the night flies and moths that were attracted to my head torch annoyed me even more as they flew into my face so I turned my head torch off and relied on Paul's. Then the rain started. As we struggled to follow the river meandering towards Bristol, out of nowhere another runner came charging past us. I have the harsh realisation that I am now once again in last position. This feels all too familiar. The minutes are ticking away into hours and I can't see any hint of being near to the city of Bristol, no lights, no buildings, just darkness and fields and silence. History was repeating itself and I began to lose hope of getting to the finish line before the 3am cut off. I thought of my son Dan who had given up his evening to be at the finish line for me. By this time he had been waiting for me for two hours which made me feel bad, I couldn't bear to let him down and have him see me being timed out. I had a mixing pot of emotions going on and I took my frustrations out on Paul which didn't help. Suddenly we were faced with a locked five bar metal gate with no way past it but over the top. With over 140 miles in my legs I somehow managed to climb over and down the other side and was happy to find that we were finally on a nice flat road with only about two more miles to go. But time was short and there was nothing for it now but to run. Once again I was almost crying through gritted teeth desperate to see signs of the finish line. I ran down main streets and took a straight line across roundabouts, surprised at how much traffic there was on the roads even at that hour of the night in the outskirts of the city. I saw the finish in the distance and gave the last bit of energy

I had to get there. My heart lifts when I see my son Dan clapping me into the finish and I cross the line at 2.42am.

Estimated finish time – between 11.30pm and midnight Saturday
Actual finish time 2.42am Sunday
Overall cumulative stopped time 1 hour and 50 minutes

Total time 44 hours 42 minutes.
38th place out of 38 finishers (32 had dropped out).

I felt devastated to have finished last again given that I'd built up a good cushion of time early on, and my stoppage time was much improved at two hours and thirty four minutes less than the time I loitered around during the GUCR. In hindsight it would definitely have helped to have previously recced the last section in daylight, as I wasn't the only one to have found the route difficult. I know of at least one other runner who admitted to using google maps to get off the field and onto the road rather than using the race route map as we did.

But like I said after GUCR, a finish is a finish and almost half of those who started didn't make it to the finish for all kinds of reasons. So I was grateful and I also achieved a personal best time by nine minutes.

The next and final race in the Canalslam takes us up north to the Leeds Liverpool Canal and it's the short one at only 130 miles.

Hiking to Everest. Little did I know that in a few months time I would have a very different mountain to climb

The most difficult route to the start line of a marathon, ever!

2013 we completed the highest marathon in the world!

2014 in Nice, France, in the grips of ME

2016 finding peace in a much slower pace of life

The very top of Mount Maroma. This symbolised so much more than the physical climb

My first race post ME. Cirencester Parkrun and I couldn't have been more nervous!

At the finish of my first post ME half marathon. The smile says it all

Completed my first post ME marathon in Malaga, just 8 months after my recovery

Celebrating after Barcelona marathon 2019

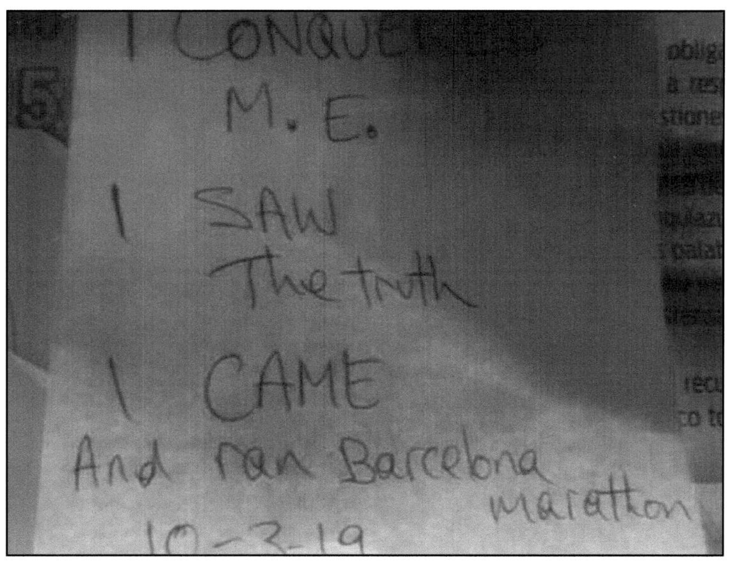

If I could have shouted from the rooftops I would have

On the Inca Trail, dancing with our guide to music being played by the locals

The start of Lima marathon in Peru. I was in the front pen!

Placing 1st LV55 at Torre Del Mar 10k

AAUT in the heat of the day, back in the zone

The start of Al Andalus Ultimate Trail 5 stage race

The wonderful Dick Kearn at the end of the canal races

In the middle of two heroes, Dick Kearn and Keith Godden, celebrating at the end of the Canalslam

Challenge complete

CHAPTER 16

THE LEEDS LIVERPOOL CANAL 130 MILE RACE

LIVERPOOL TO LEEDS AUGUST 27–28

I was running the canal from Liverpool to Leeds and I was running really well, efficiently, I felt strong and the act of running felt effortless as I was ticking off the miles with ease. Suddenly I realised that I wasn't running anywhere near a canal, and also that I hadn't seen any runners for quite some time. So I turned around and ran back for a short distance hoping to see other runners but there was no one. I then had the awful realisation that I'd run miles off course and there was no hope of making even the first checkpoint before the cut off time. I sat down feeling totally devastated and distressed because physically I felt so good, better than I had for either of the two previous canal races. But now my race had already ended before it had begun. A couple of nights later I had another dream but in this one

I was running through alleyways and buildings, up and down steps, and around sharp corners. I was running well and leading the race, but when I eventually got to the finish line I was in last place. How did that happen!

I don't ever remember dreaming with such clarity about an upcoming race before so clearly this was occupying my mind very much more than I was consciously aware.

I felt more nervous about this race than the other two because firstly, the memory of the pain of running KACR was still fairly fresh in my mind, added to that five weeks is not a lot of recovery time from running that kind of distance, and secondly I HAD to finish, the whole Canalslam depended on it. So nothing could go wrong.

With the experience of both of the previous canal races in mind I reviewed my nutrition plan and had trialled some new gels and energy products. I also decided to have more of the replacement meal drinks that I had used in KACR. Plus I had recruited a new secret weapon to my nutritional army. I had made some bread pudding a couple of weeks before the race and it was delicious, moist, easy to eat and obviously high in energy producing carbohydrates! So I made a big trayful to take with us to the race. I would need to have some savoury snacks too, so apart from Pringles, tomato soup and tomato pasta I bought some falafels and some feta and spinach pastry rolls, unfortunately my stomach decided that neither of those last two would pass my lips at any point during the race.

With this last canal race being the 'short one' at 130 miles, it struck me that it was more or less ten half marathons or five marathons. Mentally that sounded much easier to cope with. So I did some maths and decided on breaking it down into manageable chunks of a 6.5 hour marathon followed by a 7.5 hour marathon followed by three 8 hour marathons and that would get me a finish time of around 38 hours, which would be two hours inside the forty hour time limit.

Feeling as prepared physically and mentally as I could be, we packed everything, plus extras to cover all the eventualities that we could think of, into the pickup truck. We said goodbye to the dogs, leaving them in the very capable hands of our house sitters, and drove up to Liverpool.

The two hour drive turned into four hours due to an accident on the motorway which caused us to detour onto cross country roads. I hoped it wasn't going to be an omen for my actual race.

We arrived in Liverpool and, after checking into the hotel, I went to registration to pick up my number and then we went to eat. My pre-race meal for GUCR and KACR was pizza but I decided to live dangerously and break with tradition and went for the risotto instead. I like to think that this decision was the start of a much more successful race for me, but in reality it probably had nothing to do with it. Then it was back to the hotel, prepare my kit for the morning, set the alarm for 4am, rest and sleep.

As soon as the alarm went off I was up and on auto pilot. I boiled the kettle for my porridge and while that was cooling I showered. My kit was neatly laid out on the chair and once dressed I prepared my first drinks that I would carry with me. At 5.45 we headed down to the start area which was conveniently just outside the hotel. There had been some rain overnight and the street was wet and quiet, except for a growing group of runners with their crew gathering on the pavement. I felt remarkably calm, and confident in the knowledge that I had completed two 145 mile races before and this was shorter than the other two. Of course I would be returning to the pain cave again, but getting to the finish line was definitely within my capabilities.

Just before 6am Dick gave his usual race briefing followed by a short countdown to our send off. Now I could be wrong but I'm sure his final words to send us on our way were "Off you fuck then". There was a chuckle among the runners and I laughed too. The understated, casualness of these epic races is one of the things that make them so special. No big fanfare or anything like that, just a few words before sending us on our way.

Although generally you can't recover 100% from a 145 mile race in just five weeks, especially on top of another 145 mile race only seven weeks before that, my recovery from the previous two races had gone pretty well mainly thanks to the guidance of my coach, and I was feeling strong. The six and a half hour target I had for the first twenty six miles meant that I only needed to run at a fifteen minute mile pace which is barely above a walking pace. I had no strict run walk plan for this race as I'd had for the previous two, I simply kept to a very relaxed pace and walked now and again to ensure I conserved as much energy as I could for later on. I ate and drank regularly, stayed positive and focused and concentrated on getting the first marathon done.

CP1 and crew point 1 Lydiate, Liverpool (14.5 miles)
Estimated arrival time 9.37am
Actual arrival time 8.50am, departure 8.53am
Cumulative stopped time 3 minutes

I didn't waste any time as I swapped my empty bottles for full ones, topped up my snacks and gels and got running again. Paul recorded a note on his phone saying "Trin's looking good so far, I'm now off to get a coffee and a muffin for breakfast", clearly there are some nicer perks of crewing to counterbalance dealing with the smelly blistered feet of a grumpy runner. It was already getting quite warm and I was wearing black shorts and my black top from the Kennet and Avon Canal Race, which was probably not the best choice of colour to wear in the heat of the sun, especially as there was very little shade. I kept reminding myself that I have run in much hotter conditions in Spain, which is where we spend a lot of our time. My training in the Costa del Sol, and the previous year running the Al Andalus 234 kilometre 5 stage trail race where temperatures got up to 40 degrees with absolutely no shade ninety percent of the time had acclimatised me well to the warmer conditions. Giving myself these reminders quietened the anxious voice in my head about the heat and running conditions and motivated me to keep running. I went through the first marathon with time in the bank and it was nice to know I had a good buffer for later on when I would be battling the inevitable tiredness. The target for the second marathon was seven and a half hours which meant I could drop the pace to around seventeen minute miles and I was still feeling good, despite the heat.

Crew point 2 Apley Bridge, Wigan (30.5 miles)
Estimated arrival time 1.15pm
Actual arrival time 12.24pm, departure 12.34pm
Cumulative stopped time 13 minutes

Paul is ready at the crew point with a whole smorgasbord of foods laid out on the back of the truck. I had previously planned to have one of the replacement meal drinks at this point that I had tried at KACR. It was like a vanilla milkshake and to begin with I was enjoying it. But then the thickness of it started to fill me up and I thought to myself that this had to be a good thing right, all those 500 calories would surely help me over the next few miles. So I ignored my stomach telling me to stop and as I finished the whole 500ml meal drink I could already feel it on the way back up. Within a minute my stomach was empty again with all of those nutrients and precious calories soaking into the soil by the trees. So I grabbed a few more snacks for my pack, refilled bottles and took a banana to eat along the way hoping it would settle my stomach and off I went. It would be fifteen miles before I would see Paul again and in the intense heat I was getting through my bottles very quickly so I needed to stop at checkpoints between crew points to refill, sometimes even allowing myself to be seduced by the chair and have a little sit down while the lovely CP crew took my bottles for refilling.

Crew point 3 Chorley (45.6 miles)
Estimated arrival time 6.10pm
Actual arrival time 4.21pm, departure 4.39pm
Cumulative stopped time 31 minutes

The heat was energy sapping and I needed to sit down at the crew point. I changed my socks, reapplying cream to my toes and Vaseline to vulnerable areas. Paul had a mug of tomato soup ready for me which surprisingly went down very well, along with a big piece of my homemade bread pudding (recipe at the back of this book). That was purely divine! Feeling revitalised and refuelled I was on my way. Even though there were still a few miles left to cover on the first map I gave it to Paul and took the second map with me which would cover miles 49 to 77. There was one instruction at the end of the first map to cross a footbridge and Paul alerted me to it. I told him with confidence that I would be fine and that I'd look out for it. I was following another runner and when I saw a footbridge I briefly wondered if that was the one I needed to cross over. I decided that it couldn't be because the runner in front of me had carried on straight. About half a mile later I saw the runner stop and he was talking to a fisherman. It turns out that the footbridge I saw was the one noted on the map and we should have crossed over there. Apparently the fisherman had been turning runners back all day! I should learn to trust my own instincts because that simple error added a mile to the race distance and for me that could mean anything up to twenty minutes extra at the tail end of a 130 mile race. At 52 miles I came to the end of my second marathon and going by the pacing schedule I had set for my race I planned to be at that point in fourteen hours. In actual fact I had got to this point in thirteen hours so I had a whole extra hour in the bank. I decided to adjust the next three marathon targets to 8 hours, 8.5 hours and 8.5 hours which would still get me to the finish around 38 hours, two hours before the cut off. Going into my third marathon I could now drop the pace to eighteen minute miles, the pressure was well and truly off my shoulders because even though I still had almost eighty miles to go I knew I could get to the finish well inside the time I had left.

Crew point 4 Blackburn (54.5 miles)
Estimated arrival time 8.45pm
Actual arrival time 6.57pm, departure 7.08pm
Cumulative stopped time 42 minutes

I was thinking about the next crew point and decided to freshen up a bit when I got there so I asked Paul to have my facial wipes and freshen up kit ready.

Paul has set up a very welcoming crew point and I immediately sat down and took the weight off my legs and feet. As he refilled my bottles and reloaded my pack he told me that one of the residents came out and offered to make him a cup of tea, which he gratefully accepted. What a kind gesture that was!

On my food plan I was scheduled to have a pasta pot meal and thankfully, aside from the milkshake meal earlier in the day, my stomach was mostly cooperating with me on this race and I had managed to eat almost all of it. It felt good to know that I had banked some good calories. Darkness would be closing in soon so just before leaving I put on my chest torch ready for when I would need it to light my way. In the rush to leave I completely forgot about freshening up, only to remember about half a mile up the towpath. A little further on I spotted a Canal and Waterways WC so I got my little key out. I'd purchased this key at the registration of GUCR, carried it with me through the 145 miles of GUCR and the 145 miles of KACR and here at about 60 miles into the last race was the first time I got to use it, so I made the most of this golden opportunity. I had a lovely sit down wee, as opposed to the usual squat in the woods, and then a very refreshing hand and face wash. This made such a difference and I sprung out of the little hut full of the joys. A mile or so later Paul pops up unexpectedly with my toiletries bag concerned that I hadn't used it at the crew point. Obviously I didn't need it anymore but thanked him anyway. He also had a banana which I took and ate as I went so his diversion wasn't wasted. It seemed that my stomach had finally got the hang of digesting during these long races having protested and refused food during the first two.

About an hour later I noticed that it was becoming a little difficult to see and then realised that my chest torch was failing. Before the race everything that needed charging had been fully charged including the torch I was wearing and my back up head torch. The trouble was my back up head torch was with Paul because a) I'd forgotten to put it in my pack at the crew point and b) once I realised I'd forgotten it I didn't worry because I hadn't anticipated needing it. This was a rookie mistake and I certainly wasn't a rookie so I should have known better. I could see a runner ahead who had a bright head torch so I decided to try and catch up with him and share his light, and also call Paul to see if he could get my back up head torch to me somehow. I explained my situation to the other runner, and we ran together for a while. While I was happy to run at his pace he must have thought that I was able to run a little faster and he kindly offered me his spare head torch so I could run on ahead. Check Point 5 wasn't too far away and I knew that I would see Paul before it, so we arranged that I would leave his head torch at the Check Point for him to collect when he got there. Paul met me about a mile before the Check Point and then stayed with me until our next crew point, obviously handing in my running friend's spare head torch as we passed CP5. The camaraderie between runners particularly on the longer races is quite special. It was one of the main things that I missed in the years that I was ill and couldn't run. That camaraderie has been there in every ultra that I've taken part in, no matter how someone is feeling they are always there for their fellow runner.

Leading up to the crew point was a section through Gannow Tunnel that would have been tricky for me to navigate on my own and Paul had already recce'd the route so that definitely saved me some time and ensured I stayed on course.

Crew point 5 Burnley (71.4 miles)
Estimated arrival time 2.00am
Actual arrival time Midnight, departure 00.20am
Cumulative stopped time 1 hour and 2 minutes

In contrast to the day of intense heat, it had now become very cold and with moving so slowly I was starting to shiver. So I took the opportunity to change into long running tights and put a hat on, but I stayed with my short sleeves because I didn't want to feel too comfortable, I still wanted to be running periodically to keep myself relatively warm. In planning my race I had anticipated having another meal replacement drink but after what happened with the first one earlier in the day I had strangely gone off the idea. I topped up with gels and snacks instead, went through the ritual of swapping my empty bottles for full ones and headed off alone into the darkness. This was probably the most difficult section of the race, for me at least. It was deathly quiet and, much the same as at this stage in the previous two canal races, I felt tired and lonely. But it was nothing I hadn't been through before so I kept telling myself that every step forward was one step closer to the finish, the last finish line of the slam. The one good thing about running through the night is that there are more opportunities to have a wild wee because generally the only people about are runners and we were pretty spread out by then. It was just a simple case of finding a bush and remembering to turn the head torch off.

Paul met me before the crew point again because there was another short stretch where the route came away from the canal and I could potentially (translate as 'almost definitely') get lost, despite the clear instructions on the map. I have a very female brain when it comes to maps and directions!

Crew point 6 Colne (82.1 miles)
Estimated arrival time 5.15am
Actual arrival time 3.45am, departure 4.09am
Cumulative stopped time 1 hour and 26 minutes

Pre arriving at the crew point I had already made the decision to have a short nap when I got there. It was going to be my only nap during the race so I gave myself the luxury of 15 minutes. Paul woke me after what seemed like fifteen seconds and gave me a mug of hot chocolate. I'd loved to have warmed my icy cold hands around the mug but it was that insulated mug again so no heat escaped. At least the hot chocolate would warm up my core, my extremities would have to wait until the sun came up. I left the crew point wearing a nice cosy jacket, thinking that when I changed earlier I probably should have put a long sleeve top on after all.

Just before 87 miles I had to cross a bridge over to the other side of the canal and in the half-light I saw two bodies lying on the cold hard ground of the road bridge with their arms around each other in a hug. At first I thought it might be another hallucination but as I got closer I could see that it was definitely two people, and I recognised them as runners in the race. I wasn't sure what to do, I hoped they were just taking a nap and keeping each other warm while doing so. That being the case I didn't want to nudge them to make sure and wake them from their precious sleep. But what if they had just laid down exhausted in the cold and passed away? That was unthinkable, and even though they weren't moving they did look asleep. I wasn't far from my next crew point so I decided to leave them be and tell Paul to keep an eye out for the couple. I didn't need to worry though because shortly after they both came running past me. I said that I had seen them and told them about my dilemma but they laughed, one of them saying that he could sleep anywhere, he was so tired. I admit that I was relieved that I had made the right decision.

Crew point 7 Skipton (88.9 miles)
Estimated arrival time 7.20am
Actual arrival time 6.24am, departure 6.40am
Cumulative stopped time 1 hour and 42 minutes

An instant hot porridge pot was ready for me having previously requested it in favour of the scheduled replacement meal drink. Daylight had broken through and it felt good to know that I would be finished in a little over twelve hours time. It is strange how time perspectives change during a challenge like this. If my coach ever set me a training session that would last twelve hours, which I know she would never do, I have to say I would baulk at the idea of spending half a day running but with twelve hours left of this race I almost felt like I was on the home straight. Paul restocked my vest pack with drinks and snacks and gave me the very last race map that I would need, which would take me right up to the finish line. After I left the crew point Paul recorded a voice note saying, "Trin is pretty jaded, tired, in pain, but to be expected".

I was due to see Paul again after another eleven miles but the day was quickly heating up again and so was I. The cosy jacket that had kept me comfortable through the night was now an unwanted weight tied around my waist and I was running out of water. I called Paul and he moved a couple of miles closer.

Crew point 8 Skipton (97.5 miles)
Estimated arrival time 10am
Actual arrival time 9.26am, departure 9.31am
Cumulative stopped time 1 hour and 47 minutes

Paul had been to a coffee shop on his way to meet me and picked up a hazelnut latte, which really hit the spot, despite the heat. He was concerned about leaving me for another ten miles until the next scheduled crew point so planned to meet me again after just four miles to keep my drinks topped up.

Crew point 9 Bradley (101.4 miles)
Estimated arrival time 11.15am
Actual arrival time 10.44am, departure 10.46am
Cumulative stopped time 1 hour and 49 minutes

I waste no time at this unscheduled stop, just topped up my water and electrolyte drink.

With less than thirty miles to go I am struggling. The temperature had flipped back to very warm again. Every fibre in my body was telling me to stop, lie down, and sleep. My mind was trying desperately to bargain with me, just take five minutes rest and then you'll feel better. But I knew that was all lies, five minutes, ten minutes or even an hour's rest wouldn't make me feel better. I just needed to get to the finish line and then I could rest. I had downloaded some motivational quotes on my phone before GUCR but hadn't needed to look at them, until now. The quotes are by David Goggins who is a retired Navy SEAL and endurance athlete. He has also written a book entitled 'Can't Hurt Me: Master Your Mind and Defy the Odds'. As I walked along the towpath I read five or six of his quotes which quietened my mind and motivated my spirit. One quote that stayed with me and it became my mantra for the remainder of the race. It was "I don't stop when I'm tired. I stop when I'm done."

Crew point 10 Stockbridge (108.5 miles)
Estimated arrival time 1.25pm

Actual arrival time 12.55pm, departure 1.05pm
Cumulative stopped time 1 hour and 59 minutes

My stomach had finally had enough and started to reject most food but I managed to get some coke down, Pringles and a little chocolate. At this stage it was simply a case of getting whatever calories I could in to give me enough energy to keep moving. Paul kept things positive and recorded another voice note saying "Trin's doing very well, should be on a safe pace to finish well". I can't say that that was how it felt from where I was though. It was a clear case of different perspectives and despite how I felt, Paul's perspective turned out to be correct.

Crew point 11 Bingley (112 miles)
Estimated arrival time 2.30pm
Actual arrival time 2.22pm, departure 2.27pm
Cumulative stopped time 2 hours and 4 minutes

I took a five minute rest while I drank some more cold coke, it gave me enough of a sugar lift to get me moving again and I continued to repeat my mantra with dogged determination. I arrived at CP8 and topped up my water again. It was so hot and I was getting through litres of water and my electrolyte replacement drink quicker than usual. I joked with the CP crew that this is where I usually find out that I'm last (as I did in the previous two races) but they assured me that there were many runners behind me. So without wasting any more time I thank them and leave the checkpoint. I'm moving quite slowly now and my feet hurt with every step. I saw a wall and couldn't help but use it as a rest stop. It felt like it was taking forever to cover the miles and I was praying for rain to cool my skin. I messaged Paul for some support and he asked me if there was anything I needed at the next crew point but all I could think of was a new pair of legs and feet, or maybe just a spa. He replied saying he'd see what he could do. As I got myself moving again I began to feel dizzy and light headed and worried that I was about to faint so I was relieved when I finally made it to the crew point.

Crew point 12 Apperley Bridge (118 miles)
Estimated arrival time 4.20pm
Actual arrival time 4.20pm, departure 4.30pm
Cumulative stopped time 2 hours and 14 minutes

There is an ice cream van parked next to the crew point and Paul offers to get me something to cool me down but my stomach even rejects that, and normally I love ice cream, who doesn't! I managed to eat some Pringles and a few Jaffa Cakes and continue on my death march. To keep myself on some kind of pace and to occupy my mind I worked out a run/walk plan. In every mile I walked the first 0.35 of the mile, then ran to the half mile point, walked another 0.35 and finally ran to the mile mark. This felt manageable and gave my mind something else to do rather than telling me how much I was hurting and how much better I would feel if I stopped, which was all getting quite tedious and not helping at all. I felt confident that, with just twelve miles left, my finish time would be 38 hours and something, well over an hour before the cut off. Four miles on, and much to Paul's relief, I was at the final crew point before the finish.

Crew point 13 Bramley, Leeds (122 miles)
Estimated arrival time 5.30pm
Actual arrival time 6pm, departure 6.10pm
Cumulative stopped time 2 hours and 24 minutes

Paul had the medical box with him just in case I wanted him to treat my feet and although I knew that my feet were in a pretty bad condition, I felt that there would be little that he could do to ease the pain now, and it would only add time to the torture, so I made the decision to leave them alone until after the finish. As with the previous evening it had cooled down quite quickly and from feeling baked in the intense heat, I was now back to feeling cold again. I put on my lightweight jacket for the remainder of the race and said to Paul "I'll see you at the finish". Those words sounded so good!

There are little stone markers along the Leeds and Liverpool canal with distances from Liverpool and to Leeds so I knew when I was inside the last mile to the finish. As I ran/walked along that stretch of towpath I was desperately looking into the distance for the FINISH barrier and a group of welcoming race officials. I thought I saw it a few times but it turned out to be a bridge or some people walking a dog or something similar. The last mile always seems to be the longest, but eventually in the far distance I was certain that what I could see was the glorious finish line, the end to the pain, the end of the long journey that started in Birmingham in June, continued from London in July and over 420 miles later was finishing in Leeds. I managed to pick up my legs and run the last 100 metres or so to the finish line, to the cheers and clapping of the ever supportive race crew and of course Paul. One of the race directors, Dick was there and gave me a wonderful hug and put the final medal of the Canalslam over my head.

Estimated finish time – between 8pm and 9pm Sunday
Actual finish time 7.39pm Sunday
Overall cumulative stopped time 2 hours and 24 minutes

Total time 37 hours 39 minutes.
45th place out of 55 finishers (24 dropped out).

The feeling of sitting down under the tented area at the finish with other tired and victorious runners is indescribable. When I was sick with ME I thought I would never be able to run again, but here I was having trained for and finished three tough races of over a hundred miles each, inside three months. I felt incredibly proud and also extremely grateful to everyone who had helped me to achieve this amazing goal.

Paul put his phone's voice recorder close to me and asked if I had any final words. I could think of quite a few but most of them were expletives. So what I said was

"Finally, I wasn't last!

Challenge complete, and now I think I might give up running".

CANALSLAM STATS

2017 – There were 17 finishers, no women
2018 – There were 18 finishers, 1 woman
2019 – There were 19 finishers, 1 woman
2021 – There were 21 finishers, 1 woman
2022 – There were 15 finishers, 5 women

Q & A'S WITH CANALSLAM'S DICK KEARN AND KEITH GODDEN

How many times have you run the races yourselves?
Dick: I have only ever done the first GUCR, long before Canalslams were a thing. I'm afraid I can't remember how many starts and completions for the others, but I do remember Wayne started the 2005 race with 3 broken ribs!

Keith: I've run the GUC race 7 times, and finished once, the rather wet year in 2012. I'm grateful it was so wet and cold, it encouraged me to move faster to stay warm. Dick publicly announced I would be organising the 2016 event on the start line of the GUCR in 2015, so that was my last year. I may be back however.

Whose idea was the Canalslam?
Dick: I think we can safely blame Keith for that one. In 2013 Wayne had suggested doing a Liverpool to Leeds race after many years of supporting GUCR by handling bag movements – how could I refuse? LLCR was first run in

2014. When it all got too much for me, Keith kindly took on both races and soon proposed an event on the K&A. KACR was added to his portfolio in 2017 and thus the "Slam" series began.

Keith: Wayne had the idea for the canal slam name. I like to join up words to make new unique words, so it became officially Canalslam; the company name, CANALRACE C.I.C., for the same reason.

How old is the oldest male and female to have completed the Canalslam?

Keith: Currently Ellis Rust is the youngest Canalslam finisher aged 26, and the oldest is Peter Johnson, at the age of 67. Chloe Brooms is the youngest female finisher aged 28 and the oldest female finisher is Trinity Buckley… that would be me then at 59 years young.

With the canal races in mind, what's the strangest request/question you have been asked?

Dick: The best that comes to mind is Jan Soderkwist's "How heavy is the British Waterways key?" I also remember once answering my phone while standing under the Finish Banner at Little Venice, to have the runner say, "Dick, I'm at the Finish, where are you?"

What is the worst/trickiest problem that you have had to overcome in the planning and/or running of the canalslam races?

Dick: Thankfully for me, Keith has held ultimate responsibility during the Canalslam years, so he's probably best placed to answer this. I don't doubt though, that there will be many issues he'd rather forget!

Keith: Probably my worst moment was 30 seconds whilst in the cab of my hire van on the Saturday morning of KACR 2021 at the finish in Bristol whilst trying to get some sleep, after a night of getting none. I cricked my neck, and then had a focal aware seizure that lasted a half minute or so. There is quite a lot to think about, and to be concerned about, even whilst everything appears to be going perfectly well. Sleep deprivation, a good amount of brain overload, and a pinched nerve in the neck seemed to be the cause. I haven't had another since.

AFTERWORD

As I was running the last thirty or forty miles of the final race in the Canalslam I decided in no uncertain terms that this would be my last ultra race and I would only be running marathon distance or less from then on. I made this decision based on how much I was hurting and how tired I felt. Every fibre in my body wanted me to stop and my brain was doing a great job of convincing me that running these types of races over such a long period of time was not a good thing to do at my age. Besides, it told me, you've got nothing to prove.

I already had plans for the next year of running the Centurion 100 mile slam, which involved running the Thames Path 100 in May, the South Downs Way 100 in June, the North Downs Way 100 in August and finally the Autumn 100 in October. I had even already entered the first two races. But as I shuffled my way towards Leeds in that last canal race I made the decision to cancel those entries while I could still get a refund.

I was down to run the Chicago marathon six weeks after LLCR, which had been postponed from Covid year, and I thought I'd just run that for fun and then take a few months off while I figure out what I wanted to do next.

But it didn't quite happen like that. The memory of the pain drifted away leaving the feelings of accomplishment glowing inside. That old feeling of wanting another challenge stirred in me. So not only did I not cancel my race entries, I also booked two more for February and another in April.

Along with the 4 x 100 mile races, my 2023 race calendar now also includes The Pilgrims Challenge, a 33 mile run out along the North Downs Way and then 33 miles back the following day, plus the Two Oceans 56km race in Cape Town, South Africa, which has been on my bucket list since I ran Comrades.

I've been asked many questions about why and how I run ultra races. But the feeling of being an ultra runner is not easy to describe to anyone who doesn't run. At the very beginning running was a release for me and that theme has remained true, but now it's so much more. It's part of my identity, it gives me a purpose. Running challenges me, especially as I get older. Running has given me self-esteem and self-worth in abundance, something my parents never managed to do. But, as important as all of that put together, I've found my family in the running community, and within that family there have been some amazing people who have helped to steer me though some extremely difficult times. The family I have found in running is as good as any 'normal' family that I could have had, and even when I had to turn away during the years that I was ill I knew they would always be there for me when I made it back. And they were.

In 2022 I ran 2004.7 miles, 7999.6 miles since I recovered from ME. If I had actually known that on December the 31st would I have gone out and run 0.4 of a mile? Probably.

ACKNOWLEDGMENTS

Firstly I want to thank my biggest and most patient supporter Paul. Thank you for being there every step of the way from before I became ill, throughout the ME years when you held me together, to the times you walked with me through the maze to my eventual recovery. Also for all your support as I regained my fitness to the times when I would go out and spend hours training in the Andalusian mountains. I could not have completed the Canalslam without you, and your crewing was truly exceptional.

I want to thank my children and my wonderful grandchildren for being my motivation. I especially want to thank my son Dan for giving up a Saturday night to wait for hours in the cold for me to finish the Kennet and Avon Canal Race. Seeing you there at the end of that event made all the pain of the previous 145 miles worthwhile.

Thank you Ellie Greenwood for your wonderful expert coaching, for your advice and inspiration.

To Rory Coleman, thank you for doing me the honour of writing the Foreword for this book and also for your help and advice. The ULTRArace Championship years hold many special memories for which I will always be grateful to you and Jen.

To Martin Haley of Solutions Fitness for the regular sports massages which kept my muscles happy and free from injury as I continued with ever increasing mileage.

Thank you Dick Kearn, Keith Godden, and Wayne Simpson for the canal races, for providing the stage for my first major post ME challenge, and for all your support and answers to my questions for this book.

I owe a debt of gratitude to my running family who were always there for me in my darkest moments, even when I was throwing all my toys out of the pram you always patiently gave them back to me. There are too many of you to mention here and I would be worried about missing someone so I'll just say, you know who you are and I thank you from deep in my heart.

Finally there are three people who played a part in helping me to get my life back. Thank you Professor Vinod Patel for being the first person in the medical profession at the time to actually hear me and respond with great knowledge and care.

Thank you Gisela Norman for giving me periods of time when I could feel relatively normal again through acupuncture. I am certain that your treatments moved my body into a healing state.

To Anne Zipse, I feel so much gratitude to you for giving me that final piece of the puzzle in Theta Healing. What you gave me would be impossible to repay but in writing this book I hope to help and inspire others who are suffering to never give up. Believe the diagnosis, don't believe the prognosis, the answers are out there somewhere. Keep searching.

APPENDIX I
SOME USEFUL LINKS

Foreword
https://www.colemancoaching.co.uk/my-story

Chapter 2
https://www.tcslondonmarathon.com/results/history-of-the-london-marathon

Chapter 3
https://www.baa.org/races/boston-marathon/history
https://www.dickbeardsley.com/about-dick.html
https://teamhoytcda.com/the-story-of-team-hoyt/
https://kathrineswitzer.com/1967-boston-marathon-the-real-story/

Chapter 4
https://www.comrades.com/histories
https://www.southafrica.net/gl/en/travel/article/the-comrades-marathon-making-friends-along-the-road

Chapter 6
https://paultomkins.com/we-are-death-warmed-up/

Chapter 7
https://me-pedia.org/wiki/Thomas_Hennessy,_Jr.
https://www.mesupport.co.uk/m-e-information/a-short-history-of-m-e
https://www.meaction.net/countries/uk/millions-missing/
https://www.facebook.com/MillionsMissingVoice/

Chapter 8
https://www.healdocumentary.com/

Chapter 9
https://www.annezipse.com/
https://basecampspain.net/hiking-tours/la-maroma/

Chapter 12
https://www.alandalus-ut.com/

Chapters 13, 14, 15 & 16
https://canalrace.org.uk/

APPENDIX II
BREAD PUDDING RECIPE (ULTRA FUEL!)

Ingredients

450g / 1lb bread – don't cut off the crusts!
550ml / 1 pint of milk
100g / 4oz butter – melted
150g / 6oz Demerara or brown sugar
3 heaped teaspoons of mixed spice
2 eggs
350g / 12oz mixed fruit
2 heaped tablespoons of malted chocolate bedtime drink

Method

Set oven temperature to gas mark 4, 350°F or 180°C.
Break up the bread into a large bowl. Pour the milk over the bread and leave it to soak for a while.
After the bread and milk have been soaking for a while, mix it until no lumps remain.
Add all of the other ingredients and mix well.
Put the mixture into a greased baking tin and cook for 50 minutes.